D'Arcy Thompson's Ice Cream and Other Essays from *Biology Today*

Maura C. Flannery
St. John's University
Jamaica, New York

National Association of Biology Teachers
Reston, Virginia
2001

Graphic design by Michelle Finney

Cover photo by Ed Reschke

Published by the National Association of Biology Teachers
12030 Sunrise Valley Drive, #110, Reston, Virginia 20191-3409

ISBN 0-941212-29-7

Printed at Modern Litho-Print Co., Jefferson City, Missouri

THE LEADER IN LIFE SCIENCE EDUCATION

Founded in 1938, the National Association of Biology Teachers is the oldest organization dedicated exclusively to the concerns of life science educators worldwide. NABT includes more than 9,000 members from all levels of academia, business, industry, and others concerned with life science education issues. NABT empowers educators to provide the best possible biology and life science education for *all* students. As **The Leader in Life Science Education**, our members teach more than one million students each year!

Dedication

To my mother, Catherine Halley Flannery,
who taught me to write
and
To my husband, Robert Hendrick,
who gave me the confidence to do it.

Table of Contents

Introduction

The American Biology Teacher has been my publication home for many years. I have been writing the "Biology Today" column for the journal since 1982. I consider myself very fortunate to have an opportunity to regularly share my thoughts about biology and about teaching with others who are passionate about these subjects. There are so many wonderful ideas in biology, and there is a limit to how many I can inflict upon my students. My *ABT* columns give me a very special outlet for all this information.

I have tried to select essays from the past 10 years that may have continuing value, so I have shied away from those that are heavily based on recent research since they do not age well. Instead I've chosen essays that deal with the people who do biology, with issues related to teaching, and with how biology is presented in art and literature. I love to stray from biology into learning about painting and poetry and pedagogy, but I never stray too far: what I love most is being grounded in the living world. Still, I revel in the wide reverberations that biology creates in the broader culture, and I think these need to be given greater emphasis. I would argue that a deeper appreciation for biology can arise from looking beyond its boundaries.

The people who do biology are also endlessly fascinating to me, and I think their lives deserve to be known beyond names attached to discoveries in the history of science. Knowing more about them helps in appreciating how complex the problems of biology are and how rich the lives of biologists can be. As to teaching, I find it hard after 30 years in the classroom to separate biology and teaching; I crave to learn more about biology so I can teach it, and in teaching, my appreciation for my subject continues to grow. I still have much to learn about how to teach effectively, but writing about teaching helps me to clarify my goals and to see more clearly how to achieve them.

I think ideas are enriched when they are shared and so I am grateful to *ABT* editor Randy Moore for continuing to offer me the chance to share ideas, and to managing editor Chris Chantry for helping me to make those ideas as intelligible as possible. I have so many students, friends, family and colleagues who have contributed to the thoughts in this book, that I hesitate to mention them, because no matter how long a list I make, it would be difficult to name them all. But there are two people I must mention. I am grateful to Julie Upton for her encouragement and conversation, and most of all to my husband, Bob Hendrick, for creating an atmosphere in my life within which I feel very comfortable living and writing.

Maura C. Flannery

Problems in Beloit

I've just returned from Beloit, Wisconsin, where I spent a problem-filled week. It was wonderful! The source of my problems was BioQUEST, a project for the improvement of undergraduate biology education. BioQUEST's aim is to promote a research approach to learning, to foster an understanding of how biologists perceive the world. To accomplish this, the developers of BioQUEST, including John Jungck (Beloit College) who hosted the workshop, are focusing on what they call the "3 P's" — problem posing, problem solving and persuasion (Peterson & Jungck 1988). The BioQUEST project has been going on for several years with development of software to give students experience with the 3 P's. The workshop I attended brought together 20 biologists to work on curriculum in areas where BioQUEST was thought to be weak: botany, cell physiology, developmental biology and noncomputer applications.

I have rarely had such an enjoyable week, and I have never had such a rewarding professional experience. To talk about biology morning, noon and night for eight days was terrific. The organizers, along with John Jungck, were Jim Stewart and Patti Soderberg of the University of Wisconsin-Madison. The three of them did a great job of bringing together a wonderful group of people. I won't mention everyone for fear of turning this into a litany, but I learned something from each participant and from every session we had. I'll describe some of the seminars that were presented and some of the discussions we had in an effort to give you the flavor of what went on at Beloit College. It was too good an experience to keep to myself, and perhaps some of the ideas that I found so exciting will also be helpful to others.

The Three P's

The workshop began with a Sunday evening session during which John Jungck described the 3 P's. Though many of the participants had been involved in BioQUEST projects in the past, there were some like myself for whom the 3 P's were little more than a slogan. While problem solving has become a pedagogical buzzword, the other 2 P's – problem posing and persuasion – are less publicized, though they turn out to be just as important (Jungck 1991). It makes sense that you can't solve a problem until you know what the problem is. Framing a problem is often difficult for students, yet they must have some experience in doing so in order to understand how biological inquiry proceeds, as well as to solve problems. It is almost a truism in science that the most important aspect of discovery is to ask the right question. This is often difficult to do. Allowing students to confront this difficulty is one way to give them an insight into how science is done.

The 3 P's give problem solving a new twist by also calling it problem probing, which implies a more open-ended process. Problem solving implies an end point, a solution to be "found," but for many of the complex problems of science the very form of the solution is unknown. Such uncertainty is difficult for students to deal with. They want the answers; as John noted, they often ask, "How do you know when you're finished?" Problem probing is less threatening to students than problem solving. They no longer feel that there's some correct solution, but rather they are free to explore different approaches and see where these may lead. John said that this creates a "positive attitude toward error." I like this phrase. It means seeing error as a guide. You tried something and it didn't work; that's not failure because you've learned something about the problem through the probing. Error is a guide that redirects your search for a solution.

Students are so afraid of getting the wrong answer on a test that they fear all error. As long as multiple choice tests exist, that fear will not disappear. But in biology class and particularly in biology lab, students' experiences of error should be broadened through problem probing so they can come to appreciate the positive aspects of error, and to see why error is so much a part of scientific inquiry. It's hard to find the right answer when you are in the dark. Scientists spend a great deal of time exploring research paths that lead nowhere. In *Discovering,* Robert Root-Bernstein

(1989) quotes Osborne Reynold's description of his mentor, the physicist J.J. Thompson; it is a beautiful depiction of problem probing in science:

> *He would often begin with an idea which, after he had worked at it for some time, turned out to be wrong; he would start off on some other idea which had occurred to him while working on the previous one, and if this turned out to be wrong, he would start another, and so on until he found one which satisfied him, and this was pretty sure to be right. He often started out in the wrong direction but he got to the goal in the end.*

It is one thing for a student to read about such problem probing, and quite another to actually experience it, to feel the frustration and helplessness of error and the elation of shedding light on the problem. The 3 P's approach provides such experiences.

But in BioQUEST, finding the solution isn't enough. There is one more P to go: persuasion. Science, as John Ziman (1968) writes, is "public knowledge." The solution must be presented to the scientific community whose members must become convinced of the solution's validity if it is to become a part of the body of scientific knowledge. Students must learn to present their findings in a convincing way, to draw on the techniques of persuasion to make their case. They have to be able to integrate their findings with those of others and synthesize a convincing model of what is going on in the problem they are exploring. Only in this way will they see that there is more to doing science than just making discoveries; these are meaningless until they are reported, corroborated and then fit into the existing body of knowledge.

I found John's presentation interesting, but I was not yet convinced of the value of the 3 P's. I will admit to having a prejudice against the literature on problem solving. What little of it I've looked at seems complicated and rather uninteresting. Though I use some problem solving techniques in the classroom, it seems a big enough job to teach biology without teaching how to problem solve as well. As the week progressed, there were talks on each of the 3 P's and on how they could be utilized in biology teaching. Slowly, I came to appreciate how problem solving, when combined with problem probing and persuasion, could be a powerful approach in the classroom. I came to see problem solving not as a skill to inculcate as separate from biological knowledge, but rather as a way to give students some understanding of biological inquiry. Problem solving is a skill that may be useful to students in the future, but the main reason for introducing it into biology class is because it gives students a glimpse of how science is done. Biological inquiry is problem posing, problem solving and persuasion; so if we are to teach biology as more than a body of information, the 3 P's approach makes sense.

Genetics Construction Kit

As the week progressed, I became more and more convinced (persuaded!) of the value of the 3 P's. Monday morning, we worked with a computer program developed by BioQuest participants. It's called Genetics Construction Kit (GCK), and in it, students are given a number of "field collected" organisms with particular traits — drosophila traits were used. In the simplest simulation (which is, naturally, the one I opted to do), one trait such as eye color is involved. By doing crosses, students can figure out inheritance patterns: Is it a case of simple dominance or codominance, is there sex linkage, etc. This is a BioQUEST simulation, so no problems are posed, no answers given. Students must decide both what questions to ask and when a solution has been reached. Then, in writing up their work, they must persuade others that their solution is reasonable by selecting the most telling crosses.

This was the first time I'd used GCK and looking back now I can say that I enjoyed the experience. But while I was trying to figure out what was going on, what crosses to do and what the results of the crosses meant, I was working hard and feeling tense. I thought to myself that this must have been how Mendel felt as he tried to find some pattern in a sea of data. Science as a journey into the unknown became very real to me. The difficulty and frustration students may experience when using GCK are very real parts of doing science, and students need to appreciate this. But they also need guidance and encouragement in dealing with the uncertainty that is built into GCK, so the problems they confront do not create terribly negative feelings toward science. As with all instruction, the teacher has a large role to play in guiding students in their use of GCK and other simulations.

Persuasion

Over the next couple of days, we had lectures on each of the 3 P's, starting backwards with persuasion, presented by Betty Smocovitis (Stanford University). Like so many of the workshop participants, Betty has a varied background. She is a biologist-turned-historian of science, and she has also been involved in writing-across-the-curriculum projects. She began by saying that biology is a relatively young discipline. The first real university departments of biology were not established until the 1920s. Before that time, botany, zoology, genetics, etc. were seen as separate disciplines rather than as aspects of one science. Betty looks at this from a constructivist viewpoint: The category "biology" was actively constructed by individuals who persuaded others of the validity of this category. She went on to say that all of us, as biology teachers, daily continue the process of constructing biology when we decide what to teach and in our approaches to teaching.

This is quite a different way of looking at biology and stirred a great deal of discussion. But the part of Betty's talk that I found most interesting involved how a scientific paper is constructed. She quoted from the works of Charles Bazerman (1988) and Greg Myers (1990) who have done critical analyses of the language used in research reports and journal articles. They argue that scientific knowledge is constructed through written arguments, that the language is chosen to give the impression of strict objectivity and to persuade the reader of the validity of the findings. I had read Bazerman's book some time ago, and it made me a little angry and uneasy because it seemed to make scientists and their work seem less objective and more like a power play. But listening to Betty in the light of my introduction to the 3 P's, the use of language to persuade seemed more of a necessity. Science is a social process; there is a community of scientists who must be convinced to accept new knowledge and language is the primary form of persuasion among humans.

Problem Solving

The next P, problem solving, was discussed in a talk by Jim Stewart. He began by showing us a bleach container that looked like a half-gallon milk carton, but only poured when turned upside down and only released a measured amount of bleach on each pouring. Jim asked us to figure out what device inside the container was responsible for the phenomenon we'd observed. Working in groups, we tried to develop a "model" and solve the problem. After 10 minutes we hadn't come up with any brilliant explanations, but Jim used this exercise as an entry into the whole issue of how we solve problems: what kinds of models we build, how the models change as we consider more pieces of information, how the members of a group interact in model building. Jim's presentation was a good lesson in how to present problem solving in the classroom. And to emphasize the openendedness of the 3 P's, he admitted in closing that he had no idea how the bleach container worked! He was confronting the unknown along with his students.

Problem Posing

On Wednesday, Chuck Dyke (Temple University) discussed problem posing. Chuck is a philosopher by training; fields of expertise are social and political philosophy. On the face of it, he wouldn't seem to be a likely participant in a biology curriculum workshop, but he was probably the most valuable person there. I suppose you would call Chuck an amateur entomologist, but his classification skills are at least the equal of any of the biologists at the workshop. He is also an amateur farmer, so his botanical knowledge is pretty impressive too. Finally, he's well-versed in the philosophy of biology, in evolutionary theory and self-organizational theory. With this rich background, he brought a unique perspective to the group. Chuck is a thinker, and all week made comments that made us all think a little harder about what biology is and what it is to teach biology. In his talk, he gave us a number of insights into what it means to pose a problem. He said that students aren't going to be interested in asking questions – in posing problems – unless the problems are within their "cognitive space," their intellectual and linguistic space.

At first I was turned off. I loathe jargon. Since the education field is loaded with it, it is difficult to avoid it all, but I try. Cognitive space seemed to be one piece of jargon I could live without, but I changed my mind as Chuck discussed the concept. He talked about the different ways of studying insects. For example, you can study the insects in a field of goldenrod in terms of a phylogenetic tree: What are the lineages of the insects present, what are the nearest relatives? Genetics and taxonomy are important in answering these questions. But you can take the same insects in a field of goldenrod and look at them in terms of a trophic web. Then you are in a different cognitive space, and you will ask different questions: Who eats what? What is the active trophic stage? Ecology and biogeography are important in answering these questions.

Chuck went on to show how scientists in different intellectual and linguistic spaces have difficulty communicating with each, and how the same is true of teachers and students. If we want our students to appreciate what we are talking about we have to draw them into our cognitive space; or rather, we have to create a space that includes their knowledge and interests so that the questions we pose make sense to them, and so they too can pose questions that are meaningful to them and also make sense in terms of biology.

Chuck got me thinking about ways I can take students into the space called biology that I find such a pleasant and rewarding place to be. I have often thought that I would like to be able to pour my knowledge and appreciation of biology into the brains of my students. I have now replaced this obviously impossible goal with another equally impossible one: sharing my cognitive space with them. The difference is that the former is totally unrealistic, while the latter is something I can move toward.

I can at least (I hope) get to the point where our cognitive spaces have considerable overlap.

Interspersed between these lectures were other morning, afternoon and evening sessions given by workshop participants. They were an interesting group of people with a host of assets to bring to BioQUEST. They came from 20 different institutions in 12 states; all areas of the country were represented, as were many areas of biology and science education. From the very first session on, I got ideas that I can't wait to try out when classes begin again (I'm writing this in July). For example, Bob Blystone (Trinity University-San Antonio) showed us a microscopic-computer interface using the *Image* program developed by Wayne Rausband of the National Institutes of Health. This allows students to make measurements of cells and of subcellular structures, use artificial color enhancement to make some structures more obvious, and reconstruct three-dimensional views of embryos from cross sections. At another session, Betty Odum (Santa Fe Community College-Gainesville, Florida) showed us the BioQUEST computer program, *Environmental Decision Making,* which she developed with her husband, H.T. Odum. And John Kruper (University of Chicago) presented the predator-prey computer simulation *Biota,* which he helped to develop for BioQUEST. Also, Angela Collins (Florida State University) described her work on "authentic" assessment methods, ways to assess student achievement that go beyond the usual "reductionist" forms of assessment such as multiple choice testing.

Authentic assessment means such things as student portfolios, an idea I had toyed with but didn't quite know how to implement. From Angela, I learned enough about portfolios to be ready to try using them in class. A portfolio provides a way to follow a student's growth in knowledge and change in attitudes over a period of time; it allows students to show off in areas where they are particularly strong, and it gives them a feeling of ownership of the course material. A portfolio is not merely a collection of all the student's work for a semester; students have some leeway in choosing what to include. The portfolio might also include copies of articles, newspaper clippings, art work, poetry, etc., that is, anything relevant to the course's theme and subject matter. I teach a biology course for communications majors in which I try to get them to explore how biology topics are portrayed in the media, both in words and pictures. I can see their portfolios including not only their own essays and art work, but newspaper and magazine articles and perhaps even a videotape of a TV program. The very act of deciding what to include in the portfolio is a great problem for students to grapple with and involves the question of how to persuade the teacher of the value of their portfolio and of its theme.

Projects

On Tuesday afternoon, we had to break up into groups and start working on curriculum projects which we would continue to develop over the next year and which would eventually become part of the Bioquest package. Several groups fell out quickly as people with similar interests got together. One group of science educators decided to work on a program to introduce the 3 P's to in-service and student teachers. The botanists chose to create a computer simulation of how climate change would affect plant growth. The developmental biologists wanted to put together a curriculum to give students a better understanding of embryogenesis; it would utilize existing software on pattern development. The cell biologists planned to build scale models of subcellular structures and then write up directions on how these could be made by students.

That left five people, including myself, who had no idea what to do. John Jungck put us together in one group so we wouldn't feel so lonely. He instructed us to talk and come up with some ideas and then split into two smaller groups. As we outcasts began to talk, Bob Hafner (Western Michigan University) said he was interested in what a problem is, what makes a problem a problem. This struck me as a rather nebulous and uninteresting issue, but we talked — for hours, for days. It was a wonderful experience of tossing ideas around. We discovered that the five of us liked each other, worked well together, and each had something to contribute, so we agreed that we wouldn't let John Jungck split us up! We decided to develop activities based on the question: What is a problem?

Contrary to my original impression, this turned out to be an interesting and important question. It's hard to pose and solve problems if you don't know what a problem is. We used as a basis for our work an article by Thomas Nickles (1981) which Bob had brought along. Nickles has developed a constraint-inclusion model of what a problem is. In his view, constraints define the problem and characterize the solution. There are practical constraints such as those of time and money, that narrow the problems a biologist can tackle; the constraints of the biologist's expertise and mind set also come into play, as do several other types of constraints: sociocultural, theoretical, etc.

Though we've only just begun exploring the possibilities, we think that our project will be an important addition to BioQUEST. Each of us has made a contribution to the project; our group is a wonderful example of communal research. Besides Bob and me, the other members of our group are John Kruper, who brought an interest in student model-building experiences;

Anne Dehring (University of Wisconsin-Madison), who provided a wealth of experience on how students problem solve in labs; and Ann Kindfeld, (University of California-Berkeley), who has an interest in mental models and a passion for meiosis. Ann's doctoral dissertation was on the concepts and misconceptions that students develop about meiosis, and Ann now thinks of all problems in biology in terms of meiosis. It is fascinating how she can relate any aspect of problem solving to her central problem. We kidded Ann about it, but we learned a lot from her about meiosis and about how students think.

That's how I'll remember my Beloit experience, as a great mixture of learning and fun. We worked very hard, often from 8:30 a.m. to 10 p.m. (NSF got its money's worth), but we enjoyed every minute of it. Ethel Stanley (Millikin University) was the most effervescent participant and the wittiest; she was always in a good mood. Patti Soderberg was in charge of arrangements and was definitely the most energetic. Patti and Ethel kept us going; while John, Jim and Chuck kept us thinking. I can't recall another week in my life when I learned so much or was so intellectually stimulated.

The profound exhilaration I experienced made me realize how much I love biology and biology teaching, and how much I love to talk about them and to share ideas. By the time I left Beloit with my BioQUEST T-shirt (decorated with three peas in a pod, of course), I was on a BioQUEST high. I suffered several nights of insomnia before I came back to Earth and started making plans to use all of the ideas I'd collected. I've just finished 20 years of teaching and a week in Beloit has prepared me for the next 20. (*For more information on BioQUEST, please contact John Jungck, Beloit College, 700 College St., Beloit, WI 53511.*)

References

Bazerman, C. (1988). *Shaping Written Knowledge*. Madison, WI: University of Wisconsin Press.

Jungck, J. (1991). Constructivism, computer exploratoriums, and collaborative learning: Constructing scientific knowledge. *Teaching Education, 3*(2), 151-170.

Myers, G. (1990). *Writing Biology*. Madison, WI: University of Wisconsin Press.

Nickles, T. (1981). What is a problem that we may solve it? *Synthese, 47*, 85-118.

Peterson, N. & Jungck, J. (1988). Problem-posing, problem-solving, and persuasion in biology education. *Academic Computing, 2*(6), 14-17; 48-50.

Root-Bernstein, R. (1989). *Discovering*. Cambridge, MA: Harvard University Press.

Ziman, J.M. (1968). *Public Knowledge*. Cambridge, Great Britain: Cambridge University Press.

Three Friends

On a Sunday in mid-September, I spent the day in a hospital emergency room with three friends. I was the patient. Early that morning I had tripped while I was out jogging. My husband wasn't thrilled when I arrived with the Sunday paper and a rather distorted-looking right wrist. I quickly decided that I'd rather wait in the emergency room by myself than to listen to him tell me that he was always against my jogging.

Drawing from my vast emergency room experience (I come from a sickly and accident-prone family, so it is almost my second home), I knew enough to bring a book with me. I had been meaning to read about a trio of Texas naturalists, so that's how I came to have *Three Friends* with me at Franklin Hospital. The trio referred to includes J. Frank Dobie, Roy Bedichek and Walter Prescott Webb, and I first made their acquaintance in Houston, Texas, when I was there for NABT's convention in November 1990. When I travel, I like to pick up a book on the natural history or ecology of the area I'm visiting. "Sam Houston Books" seemed like a good place to find such a tome. It had a whole section labeled "Texiana," and a large chunk of one shelf was devoted to books by Frank Dobie. An author that prolific and popular seemed like a good bet, so I chose *The Longhorns*. The longhorn sounded like a Texas-style animal, an appropriate souvenir of my trip.

Longhorns

Dobie's book turned out to be great. I admit to being a dyed-in-the-wool Easterner and a confirmed urbanite, so I had a lot to learn about longhorns. I was surprised to find that the great cattle drives only took place for about 20 years, from around 1867 when the Chisholm Trail was opened to 1888 when substantial amounts of range land began to be fenced in. It was also surprising to find that the longhorn has been virtually bred out of existence. Longhorns were a great breed for long cattle drives because they were hardy and could survive on little water. The breed was derived from Mexican cattle and from wild cattle that years before had escaped Spanish herds in Texas and Mexico. These were tough beasts, well adapted to life on the arid plains of Texas.

But they were scrawny animals and produced tough meat. When cattle came to be transported to slaughterhouses, breeds that were less hardy and more meaty were selected. Dobie, who was born in the brush country of southwest Texas in 1888, could remember the stories old cowhands told of the great herds of longhorns being driven to the railroad lines. He felt a real nostalgia for these beasts; their numbers were already dwindling when he was born. At the end of the book, he writes:

> I have an immense respect for the breed. They possessed an adamantine strength, an aboriginal vitality, a Spartan endurance, and a fierce nobility that somehow makes one associate them with Roman legions and Sioux warriors.

Dobie discusses *everything* about the longhorn. He begins by describing how the breed developed and then tells how the animals were branded. Since his book is really about the whole longhorn culture, there is a great deal about the people who owned and who worked with these animals. The discussion of branding includes stories about disputes over maverick or unbranded cattle. There are also stories about life on the trail, about stampedes and raging bulls, about the uses of rawhide and of horn. The book is full of stories, and from them Dobie has built up a well rounded picture of life with the Texas longhorn in the second half of the 19th century.

A Texas Naturalist

I liked Dobie's book so much that I resolved to look for more "Texiana" when I went to Houston five mouths later for the National Science Teachers Association convention in March 1991. This time, I found Roy Bedichek's *Adventures of a Texas Naturalist*. Bedichek wrote it during a year he spent in a cabin in the Bear Creek Valley not far from Austin, Texas. The book is a series of essays on mockingbirds, golden eagles and Inca doves. But these pieces aren't just about birds. Bedichek rambles, and that's what makes his writing so interesting. In "The Golden Eagle: Soarer," he manages to discuss not only this bird's aerial feats, but the habits of jackrabbits, innate fear in animals and the behavior of animals that facilitates their extinction.

Bedichek is so interesting because he makes such unique observations. He spends two pages discussing the functions of a great blue heron's neck:

> *Fully one-third of the length of this fifty-two-inch bird is neck and bill. He is the giraffe of the bird world. And how ingeniously is this neck constructed for the work it has to do! Extended straight up, it serves as a lookout upon which to place the eyes.*

The neck vertebrae are coupled so they can swivel. This makes the neck extremely flexible; it can fold into an S-shape for flight and the head can be turned through an angle of 360-degrees. After mentioning several of the neck's other uses, including preening, Bedichek notes:

> *finally, the bird expresses affection with its neck. Herons ... twine their long, graceful necks and stand thus for hours at a time during the mating season.*

Bedichek is interested in behavior — in animal, human and even plant behavior. On a morning walk, he noticed:

> *a rock slab weighing several tons ... propped up at an angle of thirty degrees. This huge slice of white stone was in such an artificial position that I looked underneath to see what held it up. A surface root of the hackberry, against the trunk of which the monster stone was pressed, had lifted this great burden into its present position and in so doing had kindly prepared a retreat for armadillos, raccoons, opossums, or any other prowling vermin happening to need a lodging for the night.*

He goes on to explain why the hackberry is so well suited to the dry Texas hills. Water from the sporadic rainfall is held in natural seams in the stone of the hills. Only a tough, fast-growing and tenacious tree with wide-ranging roots could take advantage of these water-filled seams, and the growing roots further pry open the seams and thus "enlarge the opportunities for further growth."

Human behavior also receives Bedichek's attention. He ends the book with "Cedar Cutter," an essay about an old man he encounters in a cedar forest. The man has a large frame. As he chops down cedar trees, the remains of once well-developed muscles are obvious beneath the wrinkled skin of his bare chest. Bedichek learns that he is 86 years old and chops trees not for firewood or to make money, but because it is all he can do, all he has done his whole life. He fears that if he stops, his life too will stop. Felling trees is his livelihood in much more than a monetary sense. This encounter led Bedichek to a consideration of old age and of the difference between death in nature and in civilization:

A sharp, unsentimental surgery obtains throughout the animate world. Mother Nature wants to see her creatures healthy and happy or not see them at all. It is only in domestication that man's physical ailments are conferred upon the lower animals.

Bedichek was nearly 70 when he wrote *Adventures of a Texas Naturalist.* It was his first book, and he wrote three more before his death at age 81. You can see why the sight of an 86-year-old man chopping down trees so attracted him.

The Great Plains

While I was in "Sam Houston Books" on my second trip to Texas, I checked out the sale table (I am the type of person who looks for discount stores in Paris). That's where I found *Three Friends.* It was Dobie's name on the cover that caught my eye. Since I already had books by him and Bedichek, I decided to buy one by the last member of the triumvirate, Walter Webb. So it was back to the "Texiana" section where I found Webb's *The Great Plains.* I am embarrassed to say that, to me, the Great Plains meant little more than a great expanse of flat land out West. Webb's book has made me a little more appreciative of the ecology and the history of this large portion of our country.

He begins by reviewing the three distinguishing features of a plains environment: It has a relatively level surface extending over a large area, it is treeless and it has a subhumid climate with low rainfall. But the Great Plains is hardly a homogeneous environment. The High or Central Great Plains displays the plains characteristics in their purest forms: It is flat, treeless and dry, and it is the heart of the Great Plains. To the east and west of the High Plains are areas that exhibit at least two of the three plains characteristics. In the East, the prairie is flat and treeless, but not dry. To the West, the Plains are dry and treeless, but hardly flat.

Webb's major thesis is that the environment of the Great Plains determined human history on the Plains. He writes that:

> This land, with the unity given it by its three dominant characteristics, has from the beginning worked its inexorable effect upon nature's children. The historical truth that becomes apparent in the end is that the Great Plains have bent and molded Anglo-American life, have destroyed traditions, and have influenced institutions in a most singular manner.

Webb's book is thus a study in human ecology – how humans remade the environment and how the environment shaped human activity.

Webb argues that the technology, the political organization and the approach to the land that worked in settling lands east and north of the Great Plains were inappropriate for the Plains themselves. He says that this vast area could not be settled until new attitudes, approaches and tools were developed. For example, without forests there was no wood available for fencing. A cheap substitute was needed to cover the vast areas of the Plains; barbed wire filled the bill. Along with the windmill, it made the domestication of the West possible. The windmill provided a way to pump water to feed people, animals and plants in this arid region.

The scarcity of water, along with the poor soil found on the western Plains, had other implications. Homesteads had to be larger; a family could not eke out a living on the small plots that sufficed further east. The larger land holdings not only made cheap fencing a necessity, but meant that farmers were more isolated from each other. The close knit communities of the East could not exist on the Plains, and political systems had to adapt to these differences.

Perhaps the biggest political problem on the Plains was the distribution of water. With its abundance in the East, it was rarely the source of dissension there. Webb devotes several chapters to the search for water and the development of laws to make water use equitable on the Plains. Irrigation of farmland was unheard of in the East in the 19th century, but it was essential if any crops were to be grown on the Plains. Much litigation was involved in attempting to regulate water use. I've just been reading John Moore's (1985) article on human ecology in the *Science as a Way of Knowing* series. In it he discusses the three primary influences on plant growth: temperature, soil and water. Webb's discussion on water rights is a great example of the human ramifications of plants' need for water, and Webb's book, which Moore cites, is in a sense an extended essay on the consequences of plant distribution.

His whole book is a study in human ecology:

This volume deals with the modifications that were made by the American timber-dwellers when they emerged from the forest and undertook to make their homes on the Plains. Their effort constitutes a gigantic human experiment with an environment.

He argues that the cattle kingdom of the 1870s, which occupied practically the whole Great Plains environment, was the most natural economic and social order that the settlers had yet developed in their experiment with the Great Plains. The longhorn was well-adapted to arid conditions and sparse feed; the horse was essential to this culture because it was the only efficient means of transportation over long distances; and the cowboy's six-shooter was a necessary piece of technology because it could be carried easily and shot from a moving horse.

I grew up in the 1950s when Westerns were standard fare on television. Today's students are not as familiar with posses and cattle drives, but the story Webb tells may still be of interest to them because it is an exciting one and very much a part of American history. It is also a great example of what human ecology means: Not only do humans shape the environment but they, like all other organisms, are very much shaped by the environment and so are human tools, the technologies they use. Toward the end of his book, Webb speculates that the hard physical conditions on the Plains – the high altitude, the wind, the use of the horse, and the six-shooter – "developed through selection and survival a new and different type of man, a Westerner." Since Webb was brought up in a family that barely subsisted on the plains of Texas, that literally scraped out a living from the soil, his words have particular meaning. He probably saw himself as the product of this selection process, as a survivor, a Westerner.

Three Friends

I learned about Webb's background in *Three Friends,* a triple biography written by William Owens (1975) interwoven with letters these three friends wrote to each other. I became well acquainted with Webb, Dobie and Bedichek during my stay in the emergency room because it turned out that I was stuck there all day. An X-ray taken soon after I arrived showed that I had a rather interesting break that would require the attention of an orthopedist. It was a warm, sunny September day, and it seemed that the orthopedists had better things to do on a Sunday morning than take care of an inept jogger.

I cannot say I was happy about this situation, but at least I had my three friends with me. I got to know them quite well and discovered some surprises. I had decided to read this book after I had read one by each of the trio, so I would have a feel for them as writers before I read about their lives. All I knew about them were their names, that they were all dead, and that they were Texans. Dobie's knowledge of the longhorn and the plants and animals of the Texas Plains, Webb's understanding of ecology and Bedichek's knowledge of bird behavior led me to assume that all three had backgrounds in biology, but I was wrong. All three spent most of their lives working at the University of Texas at Austin, but none was associated with the biology department. Webb was a historian, Dobie's field was literature, and Bedichek was director of athletics.

Though they had very different occupational interests, they had a great deal in common; that's why they were such good friends. First of all, they had very broad interests. Though Bedichek was the preeminent naturalist among them, all of them took an interest in natural history, particularly the natural history of their part of Texas. As Owens notes: "All three were brought up close to nature; they were all naturalists in outlook ... All three escaped the land as a way of making a living, but they returned to it every chance they got."

Webb owned a ranch not far from Austin, and all three stayed there often. It was there that Bedichek spent his year of writing. While he was there, Dobie wrote to him often, giving him suggestions on his writing as well as observations on nature that Bedichek might be able to use in his book: "My experiences in central Texas are that the canyon wren, in his range, begins singing ahead of any other bird. The whole wren family gets out early." Webb also wrote with comments, "I have just read your second chapter, on "Co-operatives," an atrocious title which also repelled me." Obviously, their friendship was strong enough to tolerate such candor, and the title remained "Co-operatives," with a second one called "Co-operatives (continued)."

Dobie was known primarily as a folklorist. He wrote more than a dozen books that described the lore of Texas and Mexico. He was full of stories about the people and the land; nature was an integral part of these tales because these people were so tied to the land. *The Longhorns* is such a good book because it is not just a discussion of these animals, but of the people who bred, roped, branded and herded them. Webb, too, sees the whole picture. His story is a very human story, but a story of humans very much attached to the land.

It is really not surprising that I mistook them for biologists; they really were biologists: people who study the living world and its relationship with the environment. As I've said in this column several times before, I think it's important for students to appreciate that biology is not an esoteric or peculiar endeavor. It is really an everyday occupation, one that many people participate in who would not label themselves as biologists. Webb, Dobie and Bedichek all fit into this category. While their writings on nature were not formal research reports, they were undeniably students of nature.

What makes their writings so interesting is that they each bring a unique perspective to their observations. Take, for example, their writings about fences. As I noted earlier, fencing is an important issue on the Great Plains; the fencing in of the range lands brought the cattle drives to an end. Webb devotes a chapter to fences and describes how the ecology of the Plains determined the fencing methods. Without forests, wooden rail fences weren't feasible, so there were attempts to grow hedges. But the dryness, the wind and the extreme winter cold prevented the growth of species such as the osage orange, which thrived further east. These problems made the development of barbed wire a boon to farmers.

Dobie, however, describes the rise of barbed wire in rueful terms, because it was one factor in the demise of the cattle drives and of the longhorn. Once cattle didn't have to be driven long distance, the longhorn lost its edge. Other breeds could be fattened more easily and produce more meat. The fact that they couldn't have survived a long drive was no longer important. Dobie, as a folklorist, sees barbed wire as contributing to the destruction of the cowboy culture:

> Range men did not in their hearts choose to exchange free-running Longhorns, capable of rustling their own living, for fine-haired stock requiring endless attention.

He quotes an old range man as saying:

> After thirty years of settled life, the call of the trail and the open range is with me still, and there is not a day that I do not long to mount my horse and be out among the cattle.

Bedichek takes still a different view of fences; he looks at their ecological effects:

> Free and unlimited fencing has interfered with the healthy circulation of natural life, congested and confined it in pockets, restricted its channels,

*and developed conditions analogous to varices and hardened arteries in
the human circulatory system.*

He describes areas that, as a result of fencing, have been taken over by
hardy weeds such as poverty weed and Mexican tea. He does admit, however, that some fences are beneficial:

*Unconsciously, and certainly with no such purpose in anybody's
mind, the fencing-in of automobile and railroad right-of-ways has created far-reaching arboretums without which many species of plants
would have been lost, as well as the animal life depending upon them
for survival.*

Natural growth was preserved in many of these areas, and fencing here
preserves their integrity. Bedichek goes on to describe some of his observations on right-of-ways in Texas, especially the bird of life he sighted.

It was interesting, after reading their views on fences, on birds, on
cowmen and on dozens of other subjects, to get to know these three men
better through Owens' book. It was particularly nice because they turned
out to be such fine men. They were all widely read scholars who quoted
poetry as well as the daily newspapers in their letters. They were all concerned with issues of personal freedom which often put them at odds
with university administrators. They all loved Texas, especially the unpop-
ulated areas where they could have direct contact with the land and its
life. Also, they all had a sense of humor. They obviously got a kick out of
writing to each other. As Owens notes, they all lived in Austin and worked
at the same university, so they saw each other often. Most of the letters
were written when they were all in town; they just enjoyed sharing their
thoughts on paper, chiding each other for their mistakes, giving and solic-
iting advice.

Reading *Three Friends* was truly like listening in on an extended conversation, so it was a perfect book to read in the emergency room where
every patient who is conscious spends his or her time eavesdropping any-
way. But even with Dobie, Webb and Bedichek around, I grew restive after
five or six hours. I began to worry that the only doctor they could find to
set my bone was from Belmont (the local race track). Then, as I was reading about their retirement years, Dr. Miller arrived. If I had thought about
it, I should have realized that the doctor who would show up would be the
most conscientious, the one who didn't say no when the hospital called.
After a little carefully applied pressure, he put on a cast and sent me and
my three friends home.

References

Bedichek, R. (1947). *Adventures of a Texas Naturalist.* Austin, TX: University of Texas Press.

Dobie, J.F. (1941) *The Longhorns.* Austin, TX: University of Texas Press.

Moore, J. (1985). Science as a way of knowing – human ecology. *American Zoologist, 25,* 483-637.

Owens, W.A. (1975). *Three Friends.* Austin, TX: University of Texas Press.

Webb, W.P. (1931). *The Great Plains.* Lincoln, NE: University of Nebraska Press.

Lives in Science

As the new school year begins, I again ask myself the question: How did I end up here? How did I end up teaching biology instead of teaching Latin or economics or instead of becoming a concert pianist or a wealthy fashion model? The wrong genes precluded the last two options; I have my father's nose and my mother's tin ear. Teaching Latin or economics seems equally impossible because, quite simply, I'm just not interested enough to spend my life immersed in these fields. I think that teaching a subject well involves such total immersion, and this involvement, in turn, requires love of the subject. Like love for another human being, love of a subject is a very precious gift, one to savor and cherish. One way to do this is to read about others who share this love, who also feel an undying commitment to their field of study. In this column, I'd like to discuss some of the biographies and auto-biographies of scientists I've read over the past year or so. Reading of others' love of science has stirred and deepened my own. Perhaps it will do the same for you, as you begin another year in the classroom.

The Mysterious R.S.

Though I've read these books over the past year or two, I don't mean to imply that they were all recently published. Several are, in fact, old and out of print. I am a cheap person, so I shy away from the latest hardcover offerings and tend toward paperbacks, remainders and secondhand books. Not only is this approach easier on my pocketbook, but it's fun. You never know what dusty volume you'll come upon which will give you a different perspective from that found in more recent books. One of my recent favorites of this ilk is *As I Remember Him: The Biography of R.S.* by Hans Zinsser (1940), who also wrote the classic, *Rats, Lice and History* (1935). It was in the "Free, Take One" bin at our public library – the ultimate bargain. It was published in 1940 and has probably been out of print since shortly after that time. It is definitely not well-known like Zinsser's other book, and with good reason. It is a rather odd volume, since it's the biography of someone whose name is never revealed in the book, who is always referred to simply as "R.S." Zinsser writes that this mystery man, a physician and researcher specializing in infectious diseases, cooperated fully in the writing of his biography, and excerpts from his writings are woven into Zinsser's narrative.

I'm not enough of an expert on the history of such research in the early 20th century to even speculate on who R.S. might be, though obviously the mystery tantalized me as I read a 440-page book about him. The thought crossed my mind once or twice that perhaps this was a veiled autobiography, but the tone Zinsser used in describing R.S.'s personality quirks and research problems convinced me that this was indeed a biography. A couple of months after I finished reading this book, I was talking with Dr. James Coles, a physical chemist who was trained in the 1940s. In discussing books that had influenced him at the time, Coles mentioned Zinsser's book on R.S.: "I seem to remember that it was an autobiography, and that R.S. stands for the last letters of Zinsser's last and first names." I, of course, had been too dense to realize this coincidence, but knowing this made Zinsser's work that much more interesting. His descriptions of medical work in Serbia during World War I, in revolutionary Russia, and in Mexico, China and a number of other countries makes clear just how exciting a life in science can be. And his discussions of art, literature and philosophy show how broadly based it can be.

After this column appeared I received a letter from the late L.S. McClung, an emeritus professor of microbiology at Indiana University, Bloomington and a former president of NABT, who told me that he was working in Zinsser's lab at the time that Zinsser was dying of leukemia and writing *As I Remember Him*. McClung wrote that R.S. was indeed Zinsser and that the gossip in the lab was that the initials stood for "romantic self." I am very grateful to Dr. McClung for this information and for the many wonderful letters he wrote following this one.

More than Bird Watching

I began with Zinsser's book because of its strange mix of autobiography and biography. The other books I'll mention definitely fit into one category or the other. But within each category, there is a wide variety of approaches. For example, Lawrence Kilham (1988) would not label as autobiography his book *On Watching Birds*. He sees it, instead, as a series of reflections on the art of bird watching, and he is right; this book tells the story of only part of his life's work. Bird watching is his avocation, but one that he has pursued with much more than casual interest. By training, he is a physician and by occupation, a medical researcher specializing in virology. There is little in this book about that side of his life, beyond the following:

> When I started out in virology I wondered whether my amateur interest in birds might not cut in on my interest in viruses, which I also found absorbing. I need not have worried. I enjoyed the freedom of my amateur approach to birds so much that I used the same approach when pursuing viruses. As David Lack, who started out as an amateur ornithologist before becoming a professional, wrote, "It is absolutely essential that research should remain a pastime, even if it becomes a profession."

Kilham goes on to speculate about whether great scientists have broad or narrow interests. While he admits that no generalization can be made, he confesses that he's a hero-worshiper who is particularly attracted to those, whether in teaching or in research, who have broad interests. I guess I share this prejudice with Kilham and that's why I enjoyed his book so much. In it, he mentions a number of noted scientists with wide-ranging interests. One of them, coincidentally, is Hans Zinsser, whose *Rats, Lice and History* inspired Kilham to go to Harvard Medical School, where Zinsser taught. They became friends, and Kilham was impressed by how widely read Zinsser was and by his musical ability. Kilham also came to know John Enders, a scholar of medieval literature, who switched to virology through Zinsser's influence and won a Nobel Prize in medicine.

As an undergraduate, Kilham worked with Arthur Loveridge, a herpetologist, who wrote another one of my favorite books, *Many Happy Days I've Squandered* (1944), about his early years as a snake expert/British soldier in Africa. Loveridge encouraged Kilham to write about Kilham's discovery of a snapping turtle which he fished out of the Charles River in February. This article was his first scientific publication. He has gone on to publish widely in virology and in ornithology, with the latter publications indicating that he is much more than an amateur bird watcher. Throughout the book, Kilham weaves observations on birds with those on the other organisms he has patiently studied over the years. He is a biologist in the fullest sense of the word, with interests ranging from the molecular to the ecological.

Embryo Ecologist

Another biologist with wide interests was the noted ecologist Evelyn Hutchinson. As the title indicates, his autobiography, *The Kindly Fruits of the Earth: Recollections of an Embryo Ecologist* (1979), focuses on the early years of his life, up to his appointment to the faculty of Yale University. Hutchinson was born in Great Britain and educated there. His father was a chemist at Cambridge University, so from an early age he was exposed to both science and the traditions of Cambridge. His memoir is filled with observations on nature as well as references to literature and history; he is the kind of man with broad interests to whom Lawrence Kilham would be attracted.

Hutchinson's fascination with nature began early. He remembers keeping water mites and spiders in a jar when he was five, and collecting butterflies and moths before age eight. He was taught to mount specimens by a gardener who was also an avid moth collector. In a lengthy footnote to this comment, Hutchinson describes the contributions of workmen-naturalists in Great Britain; he cites four references and mentions the contributions such people have made to his work. He adds that:

> *one of the policemen in the city of York is an authority on staphylinid beetles, so this admirable tradition is still alive. The influence of such people on the history of biology in Britain greatly needs study.*

My husband, as a historian, finds footnotes fascinating. My tendency is to skip them, but Hutchinson's are too good to ignore. They are like asides in a conversation, things he just can't resist mentioning even though they don't really fit into the narrative. The tone in these asides, and in the book as a whole, is that of a friendly chat with a kind gentleman. That's how Hutchinson comes across in his writings, and that, apparently is precisely what he was. Stephen Jay Gould (1992) commented shortly after Hutchinson's death that Hutchinson was perhaps the finest person he ever had the privilege of knowing. This fine man had an exciting mind which comes through in this book and in his others. I particularly enjoyed *The Itinerant Ivory Tower* (1953), which is a collection of his essays. In it, he ranges from mouse ecology and medieval architecture to UFO's and the paranormal; it should be broad enough even for Kilham.

The Unrepentant

While I am naturally drawn to books on biologists, I don't like to get too narrow in my own interests, so I am not averse to reading about scientists in other disciplines. I bought (on sale, of course) the autobiography of the geologist F.J. Pettijohn (1984) because I loved the title: *Memoirs of an Unrepentant Field Geologist: A Candid Profile of Some Geologists and Their Science, 1921-1981*. This turns out to be a very appropriate title because, throughout his career, Pettijohn has had an undying love for fieldwork. The book's longest chapter is a wonderful description of the canoe trip Pettijohn and a friend made in 1927, when he was 23 years old. The trip took them from Minnesota to Red Lake in the wilds of Canada. As Pettijohn notes:

> *The canoe trip proved a turning point in my career. ... The trip was undertaken with no scientific goals or serious purpose, though I promised Grout [one of his former geology professors at the University of Minnesota] I would collect granites and other plutonic rocks. ... In the course of the trip I discovered, on the shores of Abram Lake, those outcrops of ancient Archean conglomerates – hitherto unmapped – that became the subject of my doctor's thesis.*

This is a good example of the fact that you are more likely to do well if you follow what interests you (something I frequently remind my students of), though this advice can be carried too far if, for example, what interests you is being a couch potato. It often leads one to a happier life in a career you enjoy.

Pettijohn truly enjoyed his career and is definitely an unrepentant field geologist. In describing his work for the United States Geological Survey, he writes that he considers these years "the most productive and rewarding of his life." Although he can't put his finger on exactly why this is the case, he thinks it involved several factors: the element of puzzle solving, the strenuous work, the "great fun" of seeing the survey map grow little by little and the contribution such maps make to the development of new theories in geology. Pettijohn enjoyed fieldwork so much that he remained committed to it even when the trend in geology was away from field exploration and toward laboratory analysis of rock. Even though he could see the value of such work, he didn't think that it should be emphasized to the exclusion of fieldwork.

Riding the Waves

Geology was also the original interest of Willard Bascom, who became a noted oceanographer. His autobiography is called *The Crest of the Wave* (1988) and is a straightforward account of his career. His story is very different from that of the other scientists I've mentioned so far. Bascom is much more heavily involved in technology and is much more of an entrepreneur. I mention his book here because I think if we confine our reading to the stories of scientists in academic settings, we get a skewed view of the scientific enterprise. Much of Bascom's work would be considered pure science; he and his colleagues discovered much about wave dynamics, the characteristics of the ocean floor and geological oceanography. But he was also involved in drilling for off-shore oil, salvaging sunken ships and underwater demolition projects for the Navy. Bascom writes well, so he makes his story very interesting. It's a nice change of pace from standard scientific biographies, and those interested in marine biology would find a great deal of fascinating material here.

Rabi

Physics has played such a large role in 20th century science and 20th century history, that if we as biologists are to call ourselves scientifically literate, we can't ignore physics completely. Yet recent studies indicate that most scientists are themselves illiterate outside of their field of specialization. I find that one way to alleviate this problem is to read physics writing aimed at the general public, for example, William Trefil's books such as *Reading the Mind of God* (1989) as well as biographical works on physicists. Two examples of the latter are books in the Alfred P. Sloan Foundation Program for scientific biographies, both with very terse titles: *Rabi* and *Alvarez*. *Rabi: Scientist and Citizen* is John Rigden's (1987) biography of Isidor Rabi, a Nobel Prize winner and one of the developers of radar.

Rabi won the Prize for his work on the magnetic properties of atomic nuclei, which he did at Columbia University. Rigden does a good job of clearly explaining the physics involved in this and other research Rabi conducted during his long career. Rigden also gives a clear picture of Rabi's personality. Rabi was a practical, down-to-earth, feisty human being. One of the stories I remember most vividly tells little about physics but a lot about Rabi's style of research. During the 1930s there was little money available for equipment so Rabi became expert at making funds go as far as possible by building his own equipment, often from used parts he managed to scrape together. He became so good at such scrounging that a foundation which had given him a $10,000 grant complained five years later when he still hadn't spent all the money.

Rigden also gives more substantial information than this, especially in describing Rabi's work as head of the research division at the MIT Radiation Laboratory during World War II. Rabi did much to accomplish the lab's main goal, the development of more accurate radar systems. He also served as an adviser to the Manhattan Project, though he turned down J. Robert Oppenheimer's request to switch from the Rad Lab to Los Alamos. Rabi felt that there was enough brain power in New Mexico and that the MIT project was too important for him to abandon it. This was the same down-to-earth approach he took to all his work.

Alvarez

In describing Rabi's work on the Manhattan Project, Rigden quotes from one of Oppenheimer's letters in which he reports on a meeting attended by a number of physicists, including Rabi and Luis Alvarez, whose autobiography was also supported by the Sloan Foundation. *Alvarez: Adventures of a Physicist* (1987) is another excellent book. Where Rabi comes across as feisty, Alvarez seems to be someone with a tremendous zest for life and for science. Since he was younger than Rabi, Alvarez's Nobel Prize winning research came after World War II. He was involved in the post-war effort to create large atoms and in the development of the bubble chamber to detect subatomic particles. But Alvarez was a working scientist throughout his career and was responsible for a large number of discoveries. His wide range of interests and great curiosity led him to participate in such projects as the use of X-rays and cosmic rays to hunt for a hidden chamber in an Egyptian pyramid. He also did work on bullet trajectories as part of an investigation of President Kennedy's assassination.

Alvarez writes that he and his wife vowed not to let the Nobel Prize change their lives, and they have never forsaken that vow, but I think the Nobel Prize did affect him in the sense that having proved himself as a scientist, he felt freer to pursue projects for no other reason than that they interested him. He is probably best known to biologists for his work later in life with his son Walter, a geologist. One day Walter showed him a piece of rock composed of a layer of clay sandwiched between two layers of limestone. The clay layer, which is seen worldwide, was laid down on the ocean floor 65 million years ago at the boundary between the Cretaceous and Tertiary periods (the K/T boundary), about the time the dinosaurs became extinct. Walter explained to him that the tiny shells of foraminifera seen in the other limestone layer aren't found above the clay layer. Alvarez writes that:

> *This was one of the most fascinating revelations I'd ever heard. ... I had not found Walter's field of science exciting before; now I did. I suggested we devise a way to measure directly how long the clay layer took to form. ... Then I remembered that meteorites are ten thousand times richer in elements from the platinum group than the earth's crust. ... I suggested we look for extraterrestrial platinum in the clay layer. A quick check showed that iridium, atomic number 77, was a better choice; it has an enormous cross section for neutron capture, which suits it better to trace-element analysis.*

What he is describing here is the beginning of the new catastrophic theories of evolution: that at times in the past the Earth was the victim of catastrophes such as the large meteorites that caused such drastic changes in the environment that large numbers of species became extinct. What he is also describing is a beautiful example of intergenerational cooperation, with both father and son being open-minded enough to accept the ideas and criticisms of the other. While there is argument over the precise scenario of these catastrophes and while some may criticize the specifics of Alvarez' work, there is no question that they developed an exciting new area of investigation in geology, paleontology and evolutionary biology.

In Praise of Rita Levi-Montalcini

I also want to mention another autobiography of a Nobel Prize winner in the Sloan Foundation Series. Obviously, I like this series. By supporting the writing of these books, the foundation has made a tremendous contribution to the development of scientific literacy in this country. All the books are well-written and none is so technical that it is inaccessible to the lay reader. I haven't mentioned all the volumes here, though some have come up in other columns. Those concerning biologists include *Advice to a Young Scientist* by Peter Medawar (1979), *The Youngest Science* by Lewis Thomas (1983), *A Slot Machine, A Broken Test Tube* by Salvatore Luria (1984) [who should have gotten a prize for the best title], *What Mad Pursuit* by Francis Crick (1988) and *The Statue Within* by François Jacob

(1988). But the book I want to talk about here is Rita Levi-Montalcini's *In Praise of Imperfection: My Life and Work* (1988).

I waited until this book was sold as a remainder because it had received mixed reviews, and I wasn't sure it was worth reading. I'm really glad I decided to get it, because I found it to be a beautiful book, both interesting and very moving. The reviewers complained that Levi-Montalcini, who received the Nobel Prize for her discovery of nerve growth factor, did not write enough about her motivations for her work, that it was solely a review of her research. In one sense, I can see what they mean. She really doesn't tell us too much about her life apart from science, but I think that this is because science is such a large part of her life. What she does do is to interweave her feelings about her work into her narrative. Though she is not very explicit about her emotions, you do get a sense of how passionately she feels about her work.

Levi-Montalcini is Jewish and Italian, and during World War II she was hiding and did her research in a tiny lab she set up in her bedroom. You have to be very deeply involved in your work, truly love it, to pursue it under such circumstances. After the war, she worked at Washington University in St. Louis with Viktor Hamburger, and it was there that she did the work involving nerve growth factor (NGF). She describes the day when she first saw the migration of nerve cell processes under the influence of NGF and tells of her elation:

> *Though in the years that followed, I was to taste the joy of discoveries of far greater import, the revelations of that day stayed permanently inscribed in my memory as marking not only the end of a long period of doubt and lack of faith in my research, but also the sealing of a lifelong alliance between me and the nervous system.*

Rita Levi-Montalcini's life in science has been a fruitful and interesting one, and all this comes through in her book.

In all the books I've mentioned here, the message comes through clearly that a life in science is a rich and exciting one. Perhaps that's why we decided to study and to teach biology. I hope that in the coming year we will be able to convey this message to our students so they can share in some way in the life of science.

References

Alvarez, L. (1987). *Alvarez: Adventures of a Physicist.* New York: Basic Books.

Bascom, W. (1988). *The Crest of the Wave.* New York: Harper & Row.

Crick, F. (1988). *What Mad Pursuit.* New York: Basic.

Gould, S.J. (1992, January). "The reversal of *Hallucigenia*." *Natural History,* pp.12-20.

Hutchinson, G.E. (1953). *The Itinerant Ivory Tower.* New Haven, CT: Yale University Press.

Hutchinson, G.E. (1979). *The Kindly Fruits of the Earth: Recollections of an Embryo Ecologist.* New Haven, CT: Yale University Press.

Jacob, F. (1988). *The Statue Within.* New York: Basic.

Kilham, L. (1988). *On Watching Birds.* Chelsea, VT: Chelsea Green.

Levi-Montalcini, R. (1988). *In Praise of Imperfection: My Life and Work.* New York: Basic Books.

Loveridge, A. (1944). *Many Happy Days I've Squandered.* New York: Harper.

Luria, S. (1984). *A Slot Machine, a Broken Test Tube.* New York: Harper & Row.

Medawar, R. (1979). *Advice to a Young Scientist.* New York: Harper & Row.

Pettijohn, F.J. (1984). *Memoirs of an Unrepentant Field Geologist: A Candid Profile of Some Geologists and their Science, 1921-1981.* Chicago: University of Chicago Press.

Rigden, J. (1987). *Rabi: Scientist and Citizen.* New York: Basic Books.

Thomas, L. (1983). *The Youngest Science.* New York: Viking.

Trefil, J. (1989). *Reading the Mind of God.* New York: Scribner's.

Zinsser, H. (1935). *Rats, Lice and History.* Boston: Little, Brown.

Zinsser, H. (1940). *As I Remember Him: The Biography of R.S.* Boston: Little, Brown.

Studies in Iconography

Iconography is a term used in art history for the study of the subject matter and meaning of works of art. It often involves tracing the history of a particular image, symbol or idea in art. The field of iconography was developed by Erwin Panofsky (1962), an art historian of the first half of the 20th century. For example, he traced the image of Father Time, so familiar on New Year's Eve, from classical images through Renaissance art to "comic cartoons and series advertisements." Panofsky and other art historians interested in iconography have contributed greatly to our understanding of how great works of art are created. The images in these works are rarely generated *de novo*, but are reinterpretations – and in some cases downright copies – of images found in earlier works.

I think an argument can be made that our appreciation for the images we use in biology could be deepened through iconographical studies. Stephen Jay Gould (1988) argues that such iconographies "offer precious insight into modes of thinking." In discussing the iconography of the evolution of the horse, Gould (1987) writes that "Scientific illustrations are not frills or summaries; they are foci for modes of thought." This is particularly true when the representation is of a concept rather than of an organism because then "the constraint of a definite 'thing' cedes directly to the imagination."

I'd like to look at both types of imagery here, at portrayals of organisms and of ideas, because both reveal a great deal about how humans have viewed the living world over a long span of time. One great example of an iconographical study of images of an animal is T.H. Clarke's (1986) *The Rhinoceros from Dürer to Stubbs, 1515-1799*. He looks at the representation of the rhinoceros in European art from the time the first rhino was brought to Europe in 1515. Albert Dürer's woodcut of the animal is one of the earliest pieces, and became the most famous and the most copied. Clarke shows that this image is found over and over again during the next 300 years. A large number of artists did not use a rhinoceros, but rather Dürer's representation of it, as the model for their work.

There are several interesting aspects of Dürer's woodcut. Perhaps the most fascinating is that at the time he executed it, he was living in Nuremberg on a street next to the armorer's quarters, and he was actively involved in designing armor. There is a drawing of a visor dated 1517 which is in many ways similar to elements of the rhinoceros's rib cage. The armor-like quality of the animal's hide in Dürer's woodcut is very apparent. The skin appears thick, and in overlapping sections, each with an ornate pattern. The legs look almost as if they are covered with mail. This highly idealized image is very different from most of Dürer's other drawings of animals which are full of very accurate detail. Colin Eisler's (1991) *Dürer's Animals* contains reproductions of hundreds of drawings, paintings and woodcuts created by Dürer – everything from a lion to a crab. Perhaps one of the reasons that his rendition of the rhinoceros is so imaginative and incorporates so many elements from his other work of the time is that he never saw a rhinoceros. His woodcut was made from a sketch sent from Lisbon where the first rhino to be brought to Europe landed.

People were fascinated by the animal both because of its exotic rarity and because of its size and shape. Dürer's drawing was copied countless times over the next 200 years. In these copies, the rhinoceros retained not only its armor-like hide, but several other aspects of the Dürer original. For example, Dürer's rhino is shown in profile. Almost every rendition reproduced in Clarke's book shows the animal in profile. These renditions run from other woodcuts to marble reliefs and even a collage of shells. The profile reveals the animal's unique shape and its bulk, so that may be why it was so popular. And I really shouldn't say "was." Though Clarke's work only chronicles the iconography of the rhino up to the 19th century, the profile view of the animal is still to be found in more modern work. A trivial but telling example is an etching of a rhino in profile on the window of a tavern in the town where I live. Though I haven't visited this establishment to investigate the origins of this art work, I suspect it's been there for some time, though probably not before the repeal of prohibition. So Dürer's image endures even into the 20th century, at least in rather kitschy forms.

Another aspect of Dürer's rhino is its inertia. This animal is just standing there, with no hint of movement. Most of the rhino pictures of the next 300 years show a similar stance and similar lack of activity. The rhinoceros is pictured as the quintessential "couch potato." Even in a painting such as Jan van Kessel's "An Allegory of Africa" in which a rhinoceros is shown using its horn to skewer the side of an elephant, the rhino is still in profile with the same inert stance of the Dürer woodcut. One reason for this posture may be that many artists never saw a rhino, so they either copied other artists' work or used the skin of the animal or a stuffed rhino as a model. If the rhino looks dead in these art works, that's because in so many cases it was. And even the living specimens were unlikely to move around much. They were in an alien environment and treated as oddities to be trooped around and gazed at. The pictures of rhinos are probably most accurate in their depiction of downtrodden and broken animals.

T.H. Clarke is not a biologist nor an art historian by profession, rather he is an art dealer who served for many years as director of Sotheby's auction house. Rhinoceros depictions had been a source of fascination for him for more than 30 years before he sat down to write this book, and his enthusiasm shows throughout it. His is not the only study of the iconography of the images of one species, but it is one of the most beautifully illustrated.

A much smaller and earlier work is Berthold Laufer's (1928) monograph of the giraffe in history and art. Laufer was a curator at the Field Museum of Natural History in Chicago, and his book covers a wider range of topics than does Clarke's. He begins his chapter on giraffe biology, and then discusses the images of the giraffe from the time of the ancient Egyptians to the 20th century. Again, as with the rhinoceros, there is a commonality among the art works cited, though copying was unlikely to be involved in many of the cases described. In a large number of the works, from a painting done in the time of Tutankhamen to a 15th-century Chinese drawing, the giraffe is shown tethered, with a human holding the rope. In the rhino pictures, the animal is rarely tied, nor is a human present. The long tether was probably used to accentuate the length of the giraffe's neck, obviously its most distinctive feature. The tether also seems to imply activity: If these animals weren't roped, they would run away. The giraffes don't seem nearly as inert and lifeless as the rhinos.

Books on animal imagery are quite popular at the moment, though most aren't serious studies in iconography like Clarke's and Laufer's books are. There is, for example, *The Artful Cat* (Bryant 1989) for feline fanciers. A book that got a lot of publicity during the last holiday season is

The Ubiquitous Pig (Nissenson & Jonas 1992). I asked for it for Christmas [that means I bought it and my husband wrapped it] and was not disappointed when I read it. It covers a wide range of porcine images from those of the English animal painter, George Stubbs [who also painted the rhino] to Porky Pig. This is a fun book, but it does make you realize how important animal images are in our visual lexicon.

Another book I got for Christmas was *The Scallop* (Woledge et al. 1957). I spotted this in a used book store and *had* to have it. This really was a gift, a beautiful one, since it has a rich red binding embossed with gold scallop shells. It was produced to commemorate the 60th anniversary of the Shell Oil Company in Great Britain, and it is a collection of essays all dealing with the company's logo, the scallop. Everything from the biology of this organism to the etymology of the word scallop is discussed; there are even recipes included, but the emphasis is on art. As Mortimer Wheeler notes, "The art of the classical world is strewn with scallop shells," and this book presents a number of examples, as well as more recent depictions. And just as there is a favored view of the rhino, there's also one of the scallop. It is rare to see anything but a side view of the shell; the organism lurking inside almost never makes an appearance.

Robert DeGraaff's (1991) *The Book of the Toad* also focuses on a single animal. Though it is beautifully illustrated, it treats more than just visual imagery. It is subtitled "A Natural and Magical History of Toad-Human Relations" and covers everything from the mating habits of toads to folk tales about these animals. DeGraaff, a professor of literature, begins his book by describing how he came to write it. He was cutting his lawn with a power mower and ran over a toad because "by the time my fingers found the switch, the blades of the mower had slashed the animal badly." He examined the dying toad and writes of this experience: "It was mostly the rush of blood that affected me, making it dramatically clear that what at first glance looked to be a clod of earth was actually a living being, unlike the cold, formaldehyde-filled frogs we had dissected in high school biology class."

DeGraaff goes on to describe how a few weeks later he came across a poem by Richard Wilbur, "The Death of a Toad," which describes a similar experience with a power mower, and "in that moment Wilbur's poem turned me into a confirmed bufophile." He then tells of an experience most of us have had with at least one topic: "In the months of teaching college literature courses that followed, I seemed to find references to toads everywhere." He decided to write an article on toads, and then had another familiar experience: He discovered that there was such a rich store of information on toads that the article expanded and expanded until it became a book.

Right now, I'm finding examples of the iconography of animals all over the place. Not long ago, while looking up an article totally unrelated to iconography, I came across a short study of the iconography of the dinosaur (Czerkas 1987). It describes an exhibit held at the American Museum of Natural History in New York on the history of depictions of dinosaurs. In the past, these animals were painted as large and lumbering, slow and plodding. But new research indicates that these animals were probably much more mobile and agile than had been supposed, and this changed thinking is reflected in changed images of these animals. The article includes several paintings of dinosaurs running through the woods and vigorously fighting off predators.

Another recent find was an article on images of chameleons (Ashworth 1984). Focusing on 16th- and 17th-century prints, it describes how Pierre Belon's woodcut of this animal became almost as durable as Dürer's chameleon. Belon had traveled to Egypt and the Middle East and had seen and drawn live chameleons. This is what made his woodcut both accurate and lifelike. William Ashworth notes that Belon's "woodcut was so striking that for the rest of the century it became the standard chameleon in zoological works." In *Prints and Visual Communication,* William Ivins (1953) describes a similar process of copying which occurred in the early herbals. Most printmakers did not use live plants as models, but rather copied the prints found in earlier herbals. Because of this, the woodcuts of plants became progressively simpler and more stylized until it was no longer possible to identify the species supposedly represented in a print. Ivins argues that such copying retarded the development of modern science, because accurate drawings of plants are needed for correct identification of species. Until it became common practice to draw from specimens, such identification was very difficult.

There are cases, however, much earlier than the woodcuts of the 16th and 17th centuries, where artists did use direct observation of nature in the creation of their works. In 1945, the British architect and art historian Nikolaus Pevsner published a book called *The Leaves of Southwell* in which he describes the sculptured leaves adorning the capitals of the columns in the Chapter House of England's Southwell Cathedral. It is a little book, on a rather small subject — leaves on columns in one part of one cathedral — but it is a treasure. Pevsner obviously cared deeply about the work that went into the building of the great cathedrals of the Middle Ages and about the minds of those who created these monuments. He sees the leaves of Southwell as significant because their creators "challenged the conventions of Early Gothic leaf decoration, and went for inspiration to nature, the nature, it seems, of the English countryside." He sees their work as the dawning of a new empiricism which eventually led to modern science. The differences between leaves of different species were accurately noted for the first time; obviously these sculptors had moved away from the general or ideal image to the specific. Pevsner parallels their work with the work of 13th-century scholars, especially Albertus Magnus, who wrote extensively and accurately on botanical subjects. The leaves of Southwell seem to reflect the written work of these medieval minds.

A less scientifically accurate figure which often appears in Gothic churches, especially in Britain, is the Green Man, a human face adorned with leaves or even made of them. William Anderson (1990) has written a book on the history of this image and traces it back to ancient times when Greek and Roman deities were often clad in leaves or even had leafy branches growing from their bodies. But the Green Man tradition is strongest among the Celts and seems to have entered medieval imagery from this source. This figure often has hair or even a beard of leaves and in some cases disgorges leaves or even whole branches from his mouth. Anderson argues that the Green Man was used so frequently in Gothic ornamentation because it was a symbol of death and rebirth. Often the face of the Green Man extends from a tree trunk symbolizing that just as the tree is reborn each spring, so will a human being be reborn in the next life. The Green Man is also a symbol of human unity with nature, and it is this meaning that Anderson sees as significant to us today. Modern artists have in a sense rediscovered the Green Man and use this image (and sometimes that of a Green Woman) as a reminder of how closely humans are tied to all of nature and particularly to the green world of plants. So, an iconographical study of this image leads from the Celtic Druids who worshiped trees to our modern concerns over deforestation.

To this point, I've looked just at the iconography of representations of organisms rather than of concepts, though the Green Man comes close to the latter. As I mentioned earlier, Stephen Jay Gould (1988) sees the iconography of concepts as particularly interesting because the imagination plays a much larger role in the depiction of an idea than of an organism. What is visible to the eye puts constraints on depictions of organisms; though often not very severe ones, if you think about how grizzly bears are turned into teddy bears. When picturing ideas, no such check with visible reality exists. As Gould notes:

How can we draw 'evolution' or 'social organization'... without portraying more of a mental structure than a physical reality?

This makes the iconography of images of concepts in science important because it is a way to investigate the kinds of thinking that went into the development of those concepts:

Iconography becomes a candid camera trained upon the creator's mind.

Images are often more revealing than verbal descriptions of concepts because, as Gould argues:

We tailor our words so carefully but reveal our secrets unconsciously in those 'mere' illustrations.

To demonstrate his point, Gould (1988) discusses the way three different biologists classified the fossil fish *Cephalaspis* and used diagrams to represent the relationship of this organism to others. Louis Agassiz, the mid-19th century zoologist who never accepted the theory of evolution, summarized 15 years of research on the relationships between fossil fish species with a diagram that showed four groups of fish, with all the species in each group branching from a single ancestral form. This diagram represented Agassiz's idea that the ancestral form had been created, and that all subsequent forms differentiated over time from these basic forms. In this scheme, Agassiz placed *Cephalaspis* as the first side branch in the most primitive group of fishes.

Eighty years later, William Patten gave *Cephalaspis* a more central place in his branching diagram of the evolution of all organisms. Patten saw this jawless fish as the link between arthropods and vertebrates. His vision of evolution was that there was one central stem from which all animals branched, and in his diagram, *Homo sapiens* is at the very top as the highest point of the central stem. Gould argues that this diagram reflects Patten's commitment to the idea of life's progressive advancement and to the claim for "linear progress as a single grand highway."

The third representation Gould discusses is Erik Andersson Stensiö's 1927 sketch of the evolution of jawless fishes. In this diagram, *Cephalaspis* is grouped with other jawless fossil fish in the Osteostraci, which is one of four branches from the primitive ostracoderms. Here *Cephalaspis* does not have the key position it held in Patten's scheme, and its position, and Stensiö's diagram in general, is more similar to Agassiz's chart.

The point that Gould makes about these three sketches is that they indicate that science can hardly be considered just a:

simple accumulation of knowledge within the unchanging framework of a universal, objective method. We did learn more and more about Cephalaspis *in particular and about the evolution of vertebrates in*

general. But the theories of Agassiz, Patten and Stensiö are three incom-
patible worldviews – three visions imposed upon our greatly imperfect
knowledge – not a progressive fleshing out of nature's bare bones.

An iconographical study of these diagrams reveals no progression, but reversion, with Stensiö's drawing being similar to Agassiz's, though Stensiö was an evolutionist and Agassiz wasn't.

In another essay, Gould (1987) does an iconographical analysis of diagrams of the evolution of the horse. These diagrams show the evolution as a linear progression from a small, dog-like animal to the massive steed of today. This depiction was originated by the Yale paleontologist Otheniel Marsh in 1874. He saw the descent of the Eocene *Orohippus* to the present-day *Equus* as "direct," with fossils providing evidence of "every important intermediate form." This idea of linear evolution became so embedded even today, that Gould notes: "In displays at our Harvard Museum, and in the American Museum of Natural History, the evolution of horses looks like a line of school children all pointed in one direction and arrayed in what my primary-school drill instructors called 'size place'."

One reason why Marsh's "ladder" became such a powerful image in the iconography of evolution is that Thomas Huxley adopted the ladder as a metaphor for all vertebrate evolution. But in the 20th century, fossil evidence mounted that the evolution of the horse was hardly linear, that there were many branches in the descent from *Orohippus*. When the paleontologist George Gaylord Simpson wrote his book *Horses* in 1951, he described the evolution of the horse as bush-like and criticized "the conceptual lock imposed by the bias of the ladder." But Gould contends that Simpson wasn't really happy about the bushiness and bemoaned the complexities that it involved. Gould also argues that this prejudice led Simpson to restrict bushiness wherever possible in his diagrams and descriptions of evolutionary development.

What Gould seems to be saying is that the simple lines of a ladder are more aesthetically pleasing than the cluttered form of a bush, and that this aesthetic difference played a role in thinking on the evolution of the horse for more than 100 years. This is an indication of the power of illustrations, a power we don't often consider.

Another example that derives from 17th-century art, and it still has a powerful effect on us today, is the image of the alchemist as seen in the work of a number of Flemish and Dutch painters. C.R. Hill (1975) has written an article with the intriguing title of "The Iconography of the Laboratory." While his discussion is not as far-reaching as the title might suggest, he does make a number of interesting points about these paintings and about how they have been interpreted by historians of science. Iconography can be a tricky business; it is often difficult to know all the influences on an artist that resulted in the choice of a particular composition rendered in a particular way.

Hill argues that the tendency of historians of science to take these paintings as factual representations of alchemists' laboratories is misguided. He classifies these works of art as genre paintings, paintings of everyday life, that were more stylized than accurate versions of the scenes portrayed. Just because painters such as David Teniers the Younger and Mattihieu van Helmont created numerous scenes in which alchemists are pictured in dark and cluttered rooms doesn't justify the conclusion, which has been made by some historians of science, that these laboratories "were seldom characterized by tidiness." These paintings reflect less the real state of these labs than the artistic traditions in which these painters worked. Hill argues that it is unlikely that they painted these scenes from life, but instead they copied old woodcuts made in the 16th century by such artists as Hans Weiditz and Hieronymous Cock. The mistake of the historians of science was to fail to do an iconographical analysis of these works of art.

I hope I've shown here that such analyses, of the images of science as well as of art, can be both interesting and enlightening. Before closing, I should mention where I got the idea for this column. It involves a book which I greatly enjoyed, and have often wanted to mention, but the occasion has never arisen. Perhaps that's because the book is a little bizarre. It's a collection of essays by William Ober (1987) called *Bottoms Up!* The title essay is an iconographical study of images of flagellation. Other studies in the book include "Can the Leper Change his Spots? The Iconography of Leprosy" and "The Iconography of *Fanny Hill:* How to Illustrate a Dirty Book." The last mentioned work may not seem very intellectually rigorous, but it is. All Ober's essays in this and his other book [with the uplifting title *Boswell's Clap* (1979)] are very scholarly and well-researched. It's just that his topics are a little off-beat, to say the least. I would not recommend these books to students (though I'm sure they'd enjoy some of the pictures), but if you want something different to read, these might fill the bill. They certainly are different, and very interesting. Ober is a pathologist who works as a medical examiner, and his hobby has been to study pathologies of the past, both mental and physical. Many of his essays deal with the ills of literacy figures, such as Boswell's sexually transmitted disease problems. The final piece in *Bottoms Up!* is on placentophagy and is absolutely fascinating.

We seem to have gotten a long way from rhinos, but I did want to give William Ober credit for getting me thinking about biology-related iconographies. After reading the *Fanny Hill* piece, I got out Panofsky's book to find out what iconography is all about (it's nice being married to an art historian), and from there I went on the trail of rhinos, giraffes and other pictorially interesting organisms. I hope this essay may get some of you started on similar adventures.

References

Anderson, W. (1990). *Green Man*. London: HarperCollins.

Ashworth, W. (1984). Marcus Gheeraerts and the Aesopic connection in seventeenth-century scientific illustration. *Art Journal,* 132-138.

Bryant, M. (1989). *The Artful Cat*. New York: Courage.

Clarke, T.H. (1986). *The Rhinoceros from Dürer to Stubbs, 1515-1799*. London: Sotheby's.

Czerkas, S. (1987). Evolving views of dinosaurs. *Natural History, 96*(12), 46-55.

DeGraaff, R. (1991). *The Book of the Toad*. Rochester, VT: Park Street.

Eisler, C. (1991). *Dürer's Animals*. Washington, DC: Smithsonian Institution Press.

Gould, S.J. (1987). Life's little joke. *Natural History, 96*(4), 16-25.

Hill, C.R. (1975). The iconography of the laboratory. *Ambix, 22*(Part II), 102-110.

Ivins, W. (1953). *Prints and Visual Communication*. Cambridge, MA: Harvard University Press.

Laufer, B. (1928). *The Giraffe in History and Art*. Chicago: Field Museum of Natural History.

Nissenson, M. & Jonas, S. (1992). *The Ubiquitous Pig*. New York: Abrams.

Ober, W. (1979). *Boswell's Clap*. Carbondale, IL: Southern Illinois University Press.

Panofsky, E. (1962). *Studies in Iconology*. New York: Harper & Row.

Pevsner, N. (1945). *The Leaves of Southwell*. London: Penguin.

Simpson, G.G. (1951). *Horses*. New York: Oxford University Press.

Woledge, B. et al. (1957). *The Scallop*. London: Shell Transport and Trading Company.

Human Ecology

Last fall, my husband went to Missoula, Montana, to present a paper. As souvenirs of this trip, he brought me two pairs of earrings, a sweatshirt with "Western Society for French History 21st Annual Conference" printed on it and two books. He said he had chosen the latter because they seemed like "my kind of books." They featured a collection of essays in which a particular locale, in this case Montana and adjacent states, was the focus of attention. That they were written by women added a bit to their appeal, as did the fact that the covers showed beautiful Western landscapes.

I waited for a few weeks before reading my gifts because I wanted to tease myself and save the treat for awhile. Finally, I started Mary Clearman Blew's (1991) *All But the Waltz* and the more I read, the more disappointed I became — disappointed and depressed. What Blew labels as "a memoir of five generations in the life of a Montana family" is made up of tale after tale of woe and hardship. It begins with her description of revisiting the rotting log cabin she lived in as a child and ends with the death of her estranged husband. In between, she tells of her grandmother who lived in an isolated cabin with her children so she could teach in a tiny village school while her husband tended the homestead all through the winter; of her mother's look of anguish when she tells her mother that she and her rather immature first husband are expecting a child; of how her father got into his truck one day, drove off across the plains, and committed suicide. What makes all this misery slightly bearable is that Blew is an extremely good writer; I stayed with the book because she described even the most heart-wrenching situations so beautifully. But I must say I was relieved when I finished the book; I couldn't take much more hardship and heartbreak.

I waited a few weeks before I tackled my other gift: Teresa Jordan's (1993) *Riding the White Horse Home.* I finally got up enough courage to start it by reasoning that no one else could have had a life as depressing and difficult as Blew's, and I was right. Jordan's book ends with a happy essay on the plans for her wedding, but before getting there I had to wade through more misery and sorrow. Her mother died when she was just starting college, and it took her years and a number of failed relationships to come to grips with this loss. There are also tales of the hardships suffered by her grandmother, who did not have a good marriage, and by her great-aunt, who did. Like Blew's book, this one is extremely well-written. That's probably what made these books so difficult to read. Each writer describes her emotional traumas and those of her kin in beautiful language, language that is extremely vivid and moving.

I found these books disappointing for a number of reasons. One reason was that they were gifts, surprises really, and surprises are supposed to be fun. The earrings and the sweatshirt turned out to be much more cheering. Also, these books had little of biological interest in them. These women seemed to be much more engrossed by human dramas than by the wonders of nature. When I read about an area with which I'm not familiar, I like to learn something about the lay of the land and about the organisms living there. I learned little about such things from these books beyond the fact that the land is so barren that ranches must be large to be profitable, and this means that homesteads are very isolated from each other. In the 1950s, Blew's parents left the only land they were able to make a go of because they wanted to be close to a school rather than arrange for their children to stay in town during the week and only return home on the weekends.

Still another reason for my disappointment was that though "my kind of book" is a collection of essays about a place or places, preferably by a woman, I like something a little more upbeat, like Sue Hubbell's (1991) *On This Hilltop* about life on her farm in the Ozarks. Yes, she gets divorced, but she has some fun, too, keeping bees and planting pansies. And Carol Bly (1981) is also divorced and trying to run a farm, as well as fight the long winters of Minnesota; she manages to maintain her sense of humor despite her problems in *Letter from the Country*.

But my disappointment in my gift books wasn't too great; it didn't stop me from buying Wallace Stegner's (1992) *Where the Bluebird Sings to the Lemonade Springs* when I was in a college bookstore. I like to look at the books assigned for courses, because you never know what you'll find. This one was used in a creative writing course; its subtitle is "Living and Writing in the West." I had never heard of Stegner, but to someone less ignorant of literature he is probably well-known because his novels have won many prizes, including the National Book Award and the Pulitzer Prize. After reading this book of essays, I'm not surprised.

Here was still another great Western writer – I should have been warned by the "West" in the subtitle – who had had a hard life. This annoyed me; I was getting sick of hard lives. My parents were immigrants who had to make lives for themselves in this country, but I don't think their lives were as miserable as the ones described in these books, or at least they kept it to themselves. And though my father died after a long illness when I was in college, I didn't see that experience as one that devastated my life, though I still miss him. But maybe that's why I don't write novels, I just don't feel as deeply as these people do. Stegner's "Letter, Much Too Late" is a letter to his mother which he wrote when he was 80, some 60 years after her death. It is a beautiful essay filled with terribly vivid memories indicating that Stegner did feel very deeply and, more importantly, could find words for his feelings.

The title of his book, which was Stegner's last (he died in 1993 at the age of 84), is a line from the song "The Big Rock Candy Mountain," which was also the title of his first novel. This song is about a mythical place, "a land that's fair and bright," where "the sun shines every day," the mountains are made of rock candy, and the springs pour forth lemonade. Stegner is fascinated by the song because to him it exemplifies the endless quest of many in the West for the pot of gold at the end of the rainbow. His father was one such seeker who never made much money but was always moving the family in an effort to finally get rich and find the good life. Six years spent on a farm in Saskatchewan and a few years in Salt Lake City, where they lived in 30 different places, were the only times in Stegner's youth when he felt any stability and sense of place. Like Jordan, Stegner's mother died while he was in college and his only sibling, a brother, had died two years before. Also, like Blew and Jordan, Stegner dealt with his troubled past by writing about it. It seems as if something in the West breeds survivors who can write about their difficult lives.

Stegner's book is different from those of Blew and Jordan in that he gives much more attention to the land. One of the major themes is that the West is being destroyed by the improper use of its very limited water resources. He argues that the needs of the land as well as those of the people must be respected, and to do this, limits must be put on population, on manipulation of the water supply and on land development. Stegner spent his life as a professor of English, but his grasp of environmental issues is sophisticated. He is also very good at describing the beauties of the West:

> *The land fell away at our feet; the sky opened like a hot air balloon filling, a gust of blue. Twenty feet below us was deep water; spread out before us was an oval lake. ... We felt, as much as saw, how infinite the sky was, with clouds and snow peaks dreaming at its edge.*

As I was finishing Stegner's books, it suddenly struck me that it is really more about ecology than I had thought, and that the same was true of Blew's and Jordan's books. They are all about ecology, human ecology; they are about how the land affects the people who live on it rather than about what people do to the land, though Stegner covers this as well. This effect of the land seems to me to be an important idea, and one that perhaps should be emphasized more than it is because I think it is a potent argument for preserving environments. Yes, destroying ecosystems means destroying species and interrelationships between species, but it also means destroying our relationship with that environment. There are any number of studies done on what human manipulations have done to eagles and wolves and frogs, but what has it done to humans? Blew, Jordan and Stegner have been very much shaped by their experiences with the lands of the West. Their works could not have been written by someone from Boston or Brooklyn. In several of his essays, Stegner discusses Western writers, why their work has not been appreciated by the nation as a whole, and why they must keep writing to attain a really mature literature of the West. He makes it clear that he sees geography as affecting the development of literature, just as it does the development of organisms.

I realize the idea that the environment affects us, as well as vice versa, isn't exactly a novel thought, but it is one that set me thinking about other books dealing with the land and how it shapes the people who live on it. In relation to the hardships of the West, one life that comes to mind is that of Martha Maxwell, a 19th-century naturalist. There is a memorable photograph of her sitting amid dozens of stuffed animals arranged in a tree-and-rock-filled setting. This picture was taken at the 1876 Centennial Exhibition in Philadelphia, where Maxwell had an exhibit that she hoped would raise money for, and interest in, her natural history museum in Denver. At this time, Maxwell was 45-years-old and had led a full and difficult life. She spent her childhood in the less developed parts of Wisconsin and then attended Oberlin College. She later married a man who sought his fortune farther west, attempting to make money on various schemes, including the search for gold. During this time, he shuttled back and forth between Colorado and Wisconsin, until Martha joined him in Denver, which was at the time a very new town. She set up a boarding house there and became more financially successful than her husband. She also pursued her interest in nature which had developed in Wisconsin but was fed by the wonders of the West. She learned taxidermy, and collected and stuffed all the animals in the Philadelphia exhibit herself. Also, she taught herself a great deal about the characteristics and behavior of these animals. But as Maxine Benson (1986) describes in her book on Maxwell, the naturalist's life was always difficult and she was always dogged by financial problems. Estranged from her husband, she sought to keep her collection together and to find a home for it after her museum in Denver failed; ultimately the effort wore her out and she died at the age of 50.

A less depressing book about the hardships of the West is Harriet Fish Backus's (1969) *Tomboy Bride*. I bought this book because of the title, which turned out to be a little misleading. Harriet wasn't a tomboy; rather, she married a man who worked at the Tomboy Mines in Nevada. She wrote this book more than 60 years after their wedding in 1906, but her descriptions of the ruggedness of the terrain and the difficulties of getting even basic supplies are detailed and vivid. This is a great book, and it's one that I read for pleasure; I didn't think I had learned anything about biology from it, but there really is a lot about how humans accommodate themselves to their environment at the same time that they are changing that environment. Harriet Backus's story also deals with other mining areas besides the Tomboy, because her husband was a mining engineer and they moved from Nevada to Idaho and into Canada as he found better jobs. This is not a harrowing tale of living hand-to-mouth like Blew, Stegner and Maxwell. Backus was successful, and Harriet and her children had the best of everything, but in a mining town that could mean living at the edge of the wilderness in a two-room cabin with no running water and supplies shipped in every two weeks. In such a situation, it is impossible for the natural environment not to have a profound effect on how you live and view the world.

But I don't think that the environment has to be quite so wild or the conditions quite so primitive for the living world to profoundly affect how you live. To me, a good example of this is Silvana Cerotti, a Tucson farmer's wife whose life is described in Elizabeth Romer's (1985) *The Tuscan Year*. You could call this a cookbook because it has a lot of great recipes in it (there's a recipe for a simple and delicious cake on page 151), but it is much more; it is Romer's description of a year in Silvana's life. Romer, who is an archaeologist and who lives in a Tuscan farmhouse that she and her husband rent from the Cerottis, writes that she decided to do this book when she went to visit Silvana one day and found her laughing as she used her new purchase, a steam iron. Romer realized that the old Tuscan ways were changing and that this might be her last opportunity to record the customs of a traditional farm wife.

Another area of Europe with equally rich culinary traditions is discussed in Roy Andries de Groot's (1973) *The Auberge of the Flowering Hearth*. This book was on sale, so I bought copies for myself and for my stepdaughter-in-law. Fortunately, Susan and I have similar tastes in food as well as in Hendrick men. She loved the copy of *The Tuscan Year* that I had given her (her favorite recipe is for pot roast and is on page 21), so I thought she would like *The Auberge* because it looked like "our kind of book," having a combination of essays and recipes. Though the essays were fascinating, the recipes are not terribly practical; almost every one of them calls for eggs and cream and butter, usually in large quantities. The auberge is in the French Alps near Grenoble. Since the area is noted for its dairy products, it is not surprising that these should show up in so many of the recipes. The cold weather and physical exertion involved in mountain living mean that the natives can afford to eat cheese and cream and butter more freely than we can, though perhaps not as freely as they do. This book was originally published in 1973. Then people might not have been quite as hysterical about cholesterol as we are today, so these recipes may have been more appealing. But it is worth wading through the calories, because de Groot's description of the work of the innkeepers and of life in the valley where the inn is situated is full of interesting details. In this context, even the food fits in.

It is interesting to contrast the traditional food of the French Alps with that of Silvana's Tuscany. Silvana uses olive oil as the fat in almost all her recipes, which aren't nearly as rich as those of the auberge. At the inn, the fat of choice is butter. In the Tuscan kitchen, tomatoes and garlic are used much more liberally than in the Alps where cream and eggs show up in recipe after recipe. But in both areas, the cooks prize freshly picked wild mushrooms and local cheeses. Silvana makes her own cheese and cures her own hams for prosciutto. The hams are stored in boxes of salt in the attic while the cheeses are hung in the grain storerooms on the second floor of the farmhouse. For the auberge, the innkeepers buy rather than make their cheeses. De Groot describes dozens of cheeses in loving detail and explains why particular ones are chosen to be served at the end of meals with particular entrees. He also describes the way wines are chosen to complement the foods, while Romer notes that Silvana and her husband are not terribly sophisticated but nonetheless drink quite good wines bought from the local vineyards. In general, the cuisine served at the auberge is more elaborate than Silvana's and that's probably why I like hers better: It is family food. But in both cases, the food very much reflects the resources of the region. Most of the ingredients are locally grown and processed. For these people, the environment, as any environment would, serves as a psychological blanket that surrounds them. It also serves as a huge environmentally rich supermarket. They are shaped not only by what surrounds them, but also, quite literally, by what goes into them.

In his last essay, de Groot wonders whether the isolated valley of the auberge will be changed if skiing in the valley is encouraged, and with it comes the development of roads, hotels and perhaps even an airplane landing strip. In a talk with one of the younger inhabitants of the village, he learns that an airplane landing strip in another valley soon fell into disuse since the way the winds whipped through made landing a plane almost impossible. And as far as development is concerned, the land owners in the valley were determined to keep their land as it was. Whether that determination held, I do not know, but obviously the hard but satisfying life in this environment had so shaped them that they might be able to stand up to the winds of change.

I will admit that this column has been a weird one. I started off with the books that annoyed me and ended up with cookbooks. But I have written this way because I've discovered that these books have a common theme: They are about people fitting into their environment. In each of these books, the environment is a major actor and a major force in the action. Ten years ago, Edward O. Wilson (1984) wrote a book called *Biophilia* describing this innate attraction to other living things that humans possess. Last year, what could be called a sequel to it was published: *The Biophilia Hypothesis* (Kellert & Wilson 1993). This is a collection of papers about the idea of biophilia, including a number of papers that present evidence for the existence of such an innate attraction. As I started to think about the effects an environment can have on the humans who dwell in it, biophilia came to mind. Perhaps one of the reasons an environment can have such profound effects on us is because of biophilia;

because we relate to the organisms in the environment, even the ones we rely on for food. In *The Biophilia Hypothesis,* there are several different viewpoints expressed on the importance of biophilia in our interactions with other living things. While Steven Kellert argues for the potency of this attraction, Jared Diamond sees it as just one of many motivations involved in our interactions with the world around us, and perhaps not a very important one. I just don't know. The feeling I was left with when I finished the book was that no one knows, but that it is a phenomenon worth further investigation. And maybe that's what I've been doing as I loll around with my cookbooks and my books of essays.

It has been below 10° F every day for the last week and there has been snow on the ground here for the past month. This is not normal for Long Island, and I'm getting sick of trying to slip and slide my way to the store over streets and sidewalks covered with ice. My environment is getting me down. It's hard to be attracted to other living things when you can't find them under the snow. It is becoming clearer and clearer to me that we are shaped by the world we live in, and right now, this seems to me the strongest argument around for conserving natural habits and preserving nature whenever we can. Yes, it is good for the organisms we save, but it is also very good for us. If the biophilia hypothesis has any validity, then the richness of our lives, and perhaps even our emotional health, is involved in our fight to save the environment.

References

Backus, H.F. (1969). *Tomboy Bride.* Boulder, CO: Pruett.

Benson, M. (1986). *Martha Maxwell: Rocky Mountain Naturalist.* Lincoln, NE: University of Nebraska Press.

Blew, M.C. (1991). *All But the Waltz.* New York: Viking Penguin.

Bly, C. (1981). *Letters from the Country.* New York: Harper & Row.

De Groot, R.A. (1973). *The Auberge of the Flowering Hearth.* New York: Ecco.

Hubbell, S. (1991). *On This Hilltop.* New York: Ballantine.

Jordan, T. (1993). *Riding the White Horse Home.* New York: Pantheon.

Kellert, S.R. & Wilson, E.O. (1993). *The Biophilia Hypothesis.* Washington, DC: Island Press.

Romer, E. (1985). *The Tuscan Year.* New York: Atheneum.

Stegner, W. (1992). *Where the Bluebird Sings to the Lemonade Springs.* New York: Random House.

Wilson, E.O. (1984). *Biophilia.* Cambridge, MA: Harvard University Press.

Notes on a Biology Watcher

It may seem superfluous to write about Lewis Thomas in a journal for biology teachers. There are a very few of us who have not read at least some of his work, and many of us have been inspired both by his ideas and by the way he presented them. But that's really why I feel the need to write about him here. His death last December just cannot go unnoted by a community that drew so much inspiration from his words, and for whom he cared so deeply.

I felt that I really had gotten to know Thomas when I read his autobiography, *The Youngest Science* (1983). I discovered that he was born in Flushing, a New York City neighborhood about two miles from my childhood home. His father was a physician; and Thomas followed in his footsteps, entering Harvard Medical School in 1933. In 1937, he interned at Boston City Hospital and learned of the medical problems facing the indigent. He notes that two major chronic diseases he had to deal with on the wards were tertiary syphilis and alcoholism, and that syphilis and tuberculosis were the two diseases people feared the most, much as we fear cancer today. He describes the amazement physicians like him experienced when they first saw sulfa drugs, and then antibiotics, bring dreaded diseases like pneumonia under control. His career spanned a time of tremendous change in medicine, but as the title of his book implies, he sees the science of medicine as still in its infant stages since so much of human disease remains very much of a mystery to us.

A Life in Research

In his autobiography, Thomas also describes his life in research. Rather early in his career in medical education he was selected for administrative assignments. He moved from one medical school to another as he received positions of greater and greater prestige and influence. He eventually became dean of the medical schools of New York University and Yale. Later, he was president of the Memorial Sloan-Kettering Cancer Center in New York. Even while serving in these positions, he maintained a laboratory and directed research on various aspects of the immune system.

There are three areas of his research I want to mention. They may not be his most important contributions, but they are the ones that interested me the most. At one point, he was studying rheumatoid arthritis and mycoplasmas, organisms that can cause this condition. Obviously, this is an important area of research relating to human health, but Thomas admits that the reason he studied this aspect of immune function rather than some other is that he enjoyed looking at mycoplasmas under the microscope because, "to put it briefly, mycoplasmas are incredibly beautiful creatures. I cannot say why they are so lovely to look at, but they are." I've written enough about the aesthetic of biology in these columns for you to appreciate why I remember this particular part of his history.

A second area of his research that seemed intriguing is the discovery made by his colleagues about how mice can use the sense of smell to recognize individuals of their species. They found that in purebred mice, a difference in a single gene was enough to allow for recognition of the scent. What makes this interesting is that the gene involved was one for a histocompatibility antigen. So it seems that the gene which allows the immune system to identify tissue is also involved in olfactory recognition.

I remember a third episode because it tells a lot about Thomas' personality. He was studying ways to modify the destruction of the kidney by bacterial endotoxin, which involves the buildup of fibrinogen in the kidney's glomeruli. He reasoned that if this buildup could be prevented, the tissue might survive. He had used a number of techniques to interfere with the buildup of this protein, and then decided to try the protease papain. This enzyme was selected because there was a jar of Adolph's® meat tenderizer, a ready source of papain, on the back shelf of a colleague's refrigerator. This rather kitchen-oriented approach to research interested me, but it was what happened next that's really fascinating. Six hours after injecting papain into rabbits, there was no reduction in fibrinogen level and no slowing of the kidney damage; but the rabbits' ears had curled over, and after 24 hours the ears "hung down over the animals' shoulders rather like the ears of spaniels."

Thomas was intrigued by this phenomenon and decided to take a detour from his kidney research and study floppy rabbit ears instead. Two years of work — including collaboration with Honor B. Fell, the British expert on vitamin A — revealed that large doses of the vitamin have a similar effect on the ears, and that both papain and vitamin A produced this effect by destabilizing the lysosomes. These organelles leak digestive enzymes that destroy collagen, the structural protein that gives rabbit ears their rigidity (1962).

At the same time that Thomas was getting entangled in the floppy ears, Aaron Kellner, who studied heart disease, had seen the same phenomenon after injecting rabbits with papain to create heart muscle damage. Unlike Thomas, Kellner chose to stay on course and not get sidetracked with ear research. The sociologists of science, Bernard Barber and Renée Fox (1958), wrote an article on Thomas' and Kellner's different responses to a serendipitous situation and what it says about styles of research. They found several reasons why Thomas chose to divert his research efforts in a new direction, including the fact that the work on the kidney seemed to have reached a dead end, and that he found the development of floppy ears in a rabbit to be a "dramatic and humorous event." I think this shows, as many of his essays do, that Thomas never took himself too seriously and was always ready to follow his hunches, even if others might find the reasons rather frivolous.

The Lives of a Cell

I suppose many of us first discovered Thomas' work with the publication of his first book of essays, *The Lives of a Cell*, which was subtitled "Notes of a Biology Watcher" (1974). The title essay develops two themes that remain very important to Thomas throughout his essay-writing career. The first is the origin of the eukaryotic cell in symbiotic relationships; in particular, the origin of the mitochondrion as a bacterial symbiont. This idea fascinates him, in part because it is so surprising; who would have thought that we carry bacterial descendants around with us in all our cells? It is also an intriguing idea because it is indicative of the intimate relationships that exist among all organisms. This is Thomas' second theme: We are very dependent on all the living things sharing the Earth with us. The operative word here is "share," a word we do not pay nearly enough attention to. We use the resources of the Earth and hardly think about sharing them with each other, let alone with other species.

Thomas is quite insistent that we humans have been very negligent in our relationship with the other creatures on Earth and with the Earth itself, but his insistence is very gentle. He is not at all strident, but rather gets his points across by using irony and wit. I did not know Lewis Thomas personally, but from his writings I think of him as a man who accepted his life and the people around him with humor and respect, and could, most importantly, laugh at himself. I think he was a good man, and I consider him a friend from whom I have learned a good deal.

I only heard him speak in person on one occasion. I have to admit that I was rather disappointed with his presentation. He did not appear to me to be a very exciting speaker; the gentle humor that is so obvious in his writing just didn't come across at the podium. This is really not that surprising. There are very few people like Stephen Jay Gould who both write and lecture well. For many writers, the written word provides a way for them to express themselves much more fully than they can orally, and Thomas seems to me to fit into this group.

Thomas' second book of essays, *Medusa and the Snail* (1979), reveals more of himself than he did in his first book, and in doing so he reveals more of his humanity. He can find a kind word to say about committees, seeing them as an indication of "the unique capacity of unique, individual human beings to comprehend each other." One essay I particularly liked, perhaps because I am an expert on the subject, is about making mistakes:

> *Mistakes are at the very base of human thought, embedded there, feeding the structure like root nodules. If we were not provided with the knack of being wrong, we could never get anything useful done.*

He then ties human error to the errors that occur in DNA, since these are also creative in that they are important for the continuance of evolutionary change.

I think one reason why so many biology teachers like his essays is that Thomas takes facts with which we are very familiar and gives them a new twist. It can get a little boring when you are teaching DNA replication for the 30th time, but nothing in biology is boring to Thomas because he looks at everything with eyes of wonder. That's what makes him such a good biology watcher; he sees a connection between DNA and human error, between mitochondria and the fate of the Earth.

I can tell how important a book is by what kind of shape it's in; the more it means to me, the worse it looks. My copy of Thomas' third book of essays, *Late Night Thoughts on Listening to Mahler's Ninth Symphony* (1983), is a mess. There is underlining everywhere, there are notes in the margins, and the binding is worn out from being pulled from the shelf over and over again. I keep it on the top shelf of my bookcase along with the *Bible,* my mother's prayerbook, and a copy of my husband's doctoral dissertation.

The Art of Teaching Science

While there are many wonderful essays in this book, the one that means the most to me is "Humanities and Science." It is a reworking of an essay that originally appeared in *The New York Times* under the title, "The Art of Teaching Science." I don't think there is any article that made more of an impression on me in terms of my teaching. Under either title, the main point of the essay is that we are teaching science all wrong. Now, since Thomas never taught high school or undergraduate biology, you might think it presumptuous of him to make such a statement, and that teachers would take offense at such audacity. But Thomas writes so convincingly, so politely, so gently — I must use the word gentle again because it is precisely the right word — that one can only agree with him and become as enthusiastic as he is about his solution to the problem.

Thomas argues that science is taught backwards; that instead of teaching students what is known about science we should tell them what is not known. He thinks this approach may be useful because the other one has failed so miserably in giving students both a true picture of science and an appreciation for science. By filling students with information, we turn them off to science because they can't absorb all that's thrown at them. We also give them the idea that science is a finished edifice. A thousand-page textbook would give anyone the impression that *everything* worth knowing about biology is already known, while, in fact, the opposite is very true, that we know very little about how the living world works.

According to Thomas, telling students about what we *don't* know would serve a number of purposes. First, it would put teachers on the same level with their students; they would all be fellow seekers for understanding, with no one having all the answers. Also, it would make science into an adventure as we all try to comprehend the world around us. Finally, this approach would lead students to expect less of science, to appreciate why all cancers cannot be cured and why environment issues are so difficult to deal with. If nonscientists have the idea that scientists know all the answers, then it is no wonder that they are disappointed with science's record in dealing with human misery, and that negative attitudes toward science develop. Thomas' approach would make such disappointment less likely because nonscientists would have a more realistic view of the limits on scientific knowledge and on the advancement of science.

I cannot say that reading this essay led me to revolutionize my teaching techniques, and that I have since become brilliant in the classroom. Miracles just don't happen, but it is true that I have not taught in quite the same way since reading this essay. I start each semester with a class in which I ask students to ask me any question they want about biology, any question at all. I am secure in doing this, because I'm sure no matter what they ask I *won't* know the answer. Last semester, for example, someone asked a question about diabetes, and of course, I could answer about insulin and the pancreas, but I could not tell the student precisely why some people develop this disease and others don't or precisely why the side effects of this disease develop as they do. No one knows the answers to these questions, and there are a great many questions like that in biology.

I do not spend the semester telling students that we don't know this, and we don't know that, about the living world. I do cover some material because I don't think I could get away with giving a test on nothing at the end of the semester. But with each topic discussed, I do make it a point to mention the areas of ignorance involved. I also try to emphasize throughout the course another major point Thomas makes in this essay: that teachers present the ideas of science as if they were somehow better, more solid, more true, than the ideas of art and literature. I think he very consciously put the humanities first in the title because he wanted to argue against this view. Besides being an accomplished researcher, Thomas was also an accomplished poet. In fact, he had poetry published in *The Atlantic Monthly* and in other magazines before he had published any scientific papers. His interest in poetry — and his understanding of the truth that only poetry can get at — made him appreciate that humans strive to understand the world around them in many different ways and that all these ways of knowing have value and can't be ranked as more or less important than any other.

Critics of Science

There is still one more point that stuck with me from this essay, which is really a gold mine of wonderful ideas. After writing on the:

deeper need to teach science to those who will be needed for thinking about it, and this means pretty nearly everyone,

Thomas adds that:

it is time to develop a new group of professional thinkers, perhaps a somewhat larger group than the working scientists, who can create a discipline of scientific criticism.

He argues that while there are a number of perceptive philosophers of science, there are no critics of science comparable to art critics such as Ruskin or literary critics such as Edmund Wilson.

He only wrote a paragraph on this subject and then dropped it, discussing it no further in this essay or in his other writings. It seems to be just a throwaway idea that he didn't consider worthy of further discussion, but to me, it is an important point. Science does need critics who will ponder the discoveries of science, put them in context, and mull over the whole question of where science is going, just as art critics do for the latest creations of the artistic community. And another function of science critics would be to put the science of today in perspective with relation to the science of the past; only in this way can we have some conceptual foundation upon which to evaluate the discoveries of the future.

Though Thomas did not spend a great deal of time on the idea of science critics, he obviously thought their function was important since he felt their numbers should be "somewhat" larger than those of scientists themselves. This is a rather astounding idea, that there should be more people interpreting and criticizing the work of scientists than people actually doing science. I think Thomas was trying to call attention to the fact that scientists are so involved with their own research that it is difficult for many of them to see the larger picture, to put their work in the context not only of other research but of the culture and society as a whole. Most scientists are so busy with their work that it is difficult for them to do this. There must be a group of people for whom their major work is science criticism, not in the sense of science-bashing, but in the sense of taking the long view of science and its implications.

The idea of the importance of science critics to the development of science and to its understanding and appreciation of nonscientists has meant a lot to me. Not that I think of myself as such a critic, but I do seek out the works of authors who seem to me to be serving this function. One of my favorites at the moment is Richard Lewontin, author of *Biology as Ideology* (1991). In this book, he dissects the implications of biological determinism as well as the consequences of the Human Genome Project. He argues that scientists want to sequence the human genome:

> *despite its limited usefulness, because they are so completely devoted to the ideology of simple unitary causes that they believe in the efficacy of the research and do not ask themselves more complicated questions.*

He sees the importance of the Project, not in its practical consequences, but "in its validation and reinforcement of biological determinism as an explanation of all social and individual variation." Such comments, such getting below the surface of research, is, I think, what Thomas has in mind when he writes of science criticism. Such criticism is very constructive in that it forces scientists to look more closely at their goals and examine their intentions; it forces them to do precisely what Lewis Thomas, perhaps our best science critic, has done: ask hard questions about where we are going in science.

While I've dwelt on "Humanities and Science" because it has meant so much to me personally, there are many other great essays in this volume. In "On Smell," Thomas mourns the passing of leaf burning and the odors it produced. In "Seven Wonders," he discusses seven problems in biology that fascinate him, from bacteria that live in thermal vents to the planet Earth itself. The last essay, which provides the title for the book, contains Thomas' ruminations on the threat of nuclear war. While this may seem far from the world of medicine and biology, it is obviously the largest threat to life on Earth and to the humanizing impulses that are so important to Thomas. He writes that he cannot listen to the:

> *last movement of the Mahler Ninth without the door-smashing intrusion of a huge new thought: death everywhere, the dying of everything, the end of humanity ... All through the last notes my mind swarms with images of a world in which the thermonuclear bombs have begun to explode.*

The Fragile Species

Thomas also writes of this theme in his last book of essays, *The Fragile Species* (1992). These essays are different from his earlier ones; they are longer and more philosophical. More and more, Thomas takes the long view as a master critic of science and applies his perceptive focus to the most distressing issues facing the human species today: AIDS, environmental decay, nuclear warfare. These are topics that are written about by a large number of people, but no one brings the combination of insight, commitment and optimism to these subjects as Thomas does. I use the word optimism because I can't think of a better one. I do not mean to imply that Thomas sees a rosy picture in which science saves us from ourselves, but rather that he sees the human species as having the capacity to deal with its problems and overcome them. This view is what makes the reader of his essays, despite their often depressing topics, feel so uplifted at their conclusion.

I think that what comes through in all his writing is that Thomas loved life, loved people, and loved learning more about both. As a hobby, he studied the origin of words, but as with all his interests, he was not content to learn about them, he had to share his knowledge with others. In 1990, he published *Et Cetera, Et Cetera,* which is subtitled "Notes of a Word-Watcher." He discusses the origin of words ranging from *love* to *human,* and in each case his wit and excitement in learning comes through. In reading this, and all his books, there is the joy of being a Thomas-watcher. The beginning of a new school year seems an appropriate time to pursue this pastime, renew our acquaintance with his work, and thus recharge our love of biology.

References

Barber, B. & Fox, R. (1958). The case of the floppy-eared rabbits: An instance of serendipity gained and serendipity lost. *American Journal of Sociology, 64,* 128-136.

Lewontin, R. (1991). *Biology as Ideology.* New York: HarperCollins.

Thomas, L. (1962). Papain, vitamin A, lysosomes and endotoxin. *Archives of Internal Medicine, 110,* 782-786.

Thomas, L. (1974). *The Lives of a Cell.* New York: Viking.

Thomas, L. (1979). *The Medusa and the Snail.* New York: Viking.

Thomas, L. (1983). *The Youngest Science.* New York: Viking.

Thomas, L. (1983). *Late Night Thoughts on Listening to Mahler's Ninth Symphony.* New York: Viking.

Thomas, L. (1990). *Et Cetera, Et Cetera.* Boston: Little, Brown.

Thomas, L. (1992). *The Fragile Species.* New York: Scribner's.

Birdmen

The title of this column might seem rather sexist. After all, there are many women who are ornithologists and even more who are amateur bird watchers, so why focus on the men? Quite simply, it's because I want to devote this column to two of my favorite writers about birds who just happen to be men: Lawrence Kilham and Alexander Skutch. I have read several books by each of these authors and have fallen in love with the way they mix hard evidence on bird behavior with admiration for the organisms they are studying. Since I plan to discuss primarily their work, I couldn't find a more appropriate — or succinct — title than "Birdmen."

Lawrence Kilham

On several occasions, I have mentioned that I came to read a particular book because I happened to get it at a rock-bottom price. This may seem like a rather anti-intellectual way to choose reading material, but it has worked to my benefit on several occasions. I had seen Lawrence Kilham's book *On Watching Birds* (1988) advertised, but I had no real desire to buy it. I am not a bird watcher, and the title implied that this was a manual on how to pursue this popular hobby. But when I found it on a remainder table at $1.50, I was willing to take a chance, especially when I discovered it contained a chapter on one of my favorite topics, "Instinct for Beauty and Love of Animals."

Though *On Watching Birds* does contain some advice for those who wish to spend time observing animals, it turned out to be a personal memoir of someone who might be called an amateur ornithologist rather than just a bird watcher. Kilham is a retired virologist who developed a love of nature early in life. He went to Harvard as a zoology major, but turned to history and literature before going on to medical school. His interest in birds intensified when he married because his wife Jane, also a physician, is an avid bird watcher. After service in World War II, Kilham worked with John Enders, who received the Nobel Prize for his research on growing the polio virus in culture. Kilham studied the mumps virus, moving on to the National Institutes of Health in 1949 and eventually to Dartmouth in the 1960s, where he worked on the relationship between viruses and cancer.

All this time, Kilham was also a serious bird watcher. He writes that early in his career he wondered if his interest in birds would cut into his interest in viruses, but he found that:

> I need not have worried. I enjoyed the freedom of my amateur approach to birds so much that I used the same approach when pursuing viruses (p. 115).

He found that when things weren't going well in his viral research, his productivity in bird work went up and vice versa, so he always had some work to encourage him to keep going in both areas.

In a 1964 article on Kilham in the *Dartmouth Alumni Magazine,* George O'Connell writes that over Kilham's desk is the maxim: leisure is the mother of discovery. For Kilham, this leisure involved him not only in virology and bird watching, but also in the history of medicine, particularly in the work of physician-naturalists. All these forms of leisure were very fruitful for Kilham. He lectured on the history of medicine to medical students, received a Research Career Award from Dartmouth on his viral work, and published numerous articles on bird behavior in ornithology journals. Wherever he was working — or vacationing — he and Jane took time to study birds. In Costa Rica, he found the heat difficult to take, but:

> I think these initial difficulties made what we found later the more enjoyable. Adaptation made the difference. Whereas at home walking makes me feel better, at Palo Verde it made me feel worse. And, mirabile dictu, the less I walked about, the more I saw (p. 62).

On Sapelo, an island off the coast of Georgia, he studied pileated woodpeckers, and in Africa, he observed the behavior of white casqued hornbills near Entebbe. He writes that from the hornbills he learned that:

> I succeed best with opportunistic studies, topics that fit in with the country where I am living and with work I am doing (p. 21).

Perhaps it is because woodpeckers can be found in both the north and the south that they became the focus of many of Kilham's observations. He recalls that these studies began in 1956 when he was walking near the Chesapeake and Ohio Canal in Maryland wondering if he could find birds in the United States that would be as engrossing as the hornbills had been in Africa. As he was considering this problem, he saw some blue jays trying to steal acorns from red-headed woodpeckers.

Then an idea came to me. Why go farther? Why not study these birds? Keep with them, I said to myself, and something will turn up (p. 32).

He kept with them even as he vacationed in Florida and later moved to New Hampshire, so he was able to observe a variety of species. While at Dartmouth, he spent at least an hour a day observing woodpeckers and other species in a woodlot near his home. These observations led to the book, *Woodpeckers of Eastern North America* (1983), which is a thorough guide to several woodpecker species.

Kilham's work on birds intensified when he retired from Dartmouth at the age of 70 in 1980. He then began extensive observations on crows and ravens, and in 1989 published *The American Crow and the Common Raven*. The book contains a wealth of information on these birds, but it is also a very personal book which makes it much more than a monograph on bird behavior. For example, Kilham discusses his experiences with hand-raised ravens. He manages to convey his love for these creatures while also noting that he made significant observations on their behavior such as those on a raven he raised which had the rather unimaginative name of Raveny:

One of Raveny's steadier occupations was storing food and objects. He tried to do so within a few weeks of fledgling, but had difficulties finding suitable covering materials ... The amount of effort he put into catching was related to how much he prized what he carried (p. 205).

Like many other observers, Kilham notes the intelligence of crows. In his book, he tries to show that "crows think consciously and make decisions as part of their daily lives" (p. 169). Tail pulling is a common habit among crows. A crow can rob another by pulling its tail. Crows also work together. In mobbing, a number of crows caw together as they pursue, surround, or face either other crows in territorial disputes or predators that are particularly threatening. Kilham is also one of the few to observe anting among American crows in the wild. In this behavior, a crow takes ants in its beak and rubs them into its skin. This rather odd behavior seems to be a way to control feather mites and soothe skin irritations. [I am reminded here of David Quammen, a good nature writer with a rather ironical tone, who has a tongue-in-cheek essay on anting in crows (1985). Quammen attributes this behavior to the crows' intelligence: they are easily bored and the stimulation they get from anting is somewhat akin to drug use in the young people.]

While Kilham's observations on birds are fascinating, what interests me most about his writing are the insights he gives into why he studies nature in the way he does and why he derives so much pleasure from it. I say "studies nature" rather than "studies birds" because Kilham hardly limits himself to feathered creatures. He writes that:

> readers may wonder why, in a book on watching bird behavior, I occasionally give an account of watching some mammals. I feel that it does not pay to be too narrowly focused (1988, p. 24).

He also writes about a problem with this approach:

> There is probably no greater barrier for most people to watching birds or animals, or to studying anything else, for that matter, than the idea of being alone (1988, p. 163).

Because of his desire for solitude, Kilham and his wife often make their observations separately. This has the added benefit of giving them a great deal to tell each other at the end of the day. Kilham also argues that when you are studying nature, you are never really alone because you experience a oneness with other life.

At the close of his book, Kilham writes that what he likes about behavior-watching is that it "not only strengthens my bonds with the beauty of nature, but also my empathy with living things" (1988, p. 171). It is ultimately this empathy that makes Kilham such a good observer of behavior; he identifies with his subjects so closely that he is able to glean a great deal from his observations.

Alexander Skutch

Empathy with his subjects is also a hallmark of Alexander Skutch's work. I first encountered Skutch through an article he wrote called "Miniatures and Giants" (1983a). It was about the influence of size on biological form and function. There I found some novel ideas on the problems of very large and very small animals. I next read Skutch's book, *Life Ascending* (1985), in which he discusses evolution from the point of view of increasing sensitivity of the senses. But it was when I read his *Nature through Tropical Windows* (1983b) that I decided I wanted to write about

Skutch. In it, he describes what he can observe from his home in a forest clearing in Costa Rica. I particularly liked the chapters on the exploits, over a number of years, of a family of house wrens.

Skutch received a doctorate in botany from Johns Hopkins University in 1928. He then went to Panama on a fellowship for botanical research, and while there, became fascinated with the birds of the area:

> Looking into the subject after my return to well-stocked libraries, I learned that the birds of Central America had been so thoroughly collected and described that the probability of finding new species was remote but that very little was known about the lives of these beautiful creatures (p. 3).

So, like Kilham, Skutch became a student of bird behavior. As his interests shifted from botany to ornithology, the Depression made it difficult to get research support. While museums were willing to spend money on bird specimens, Skutch found killing birds for this purpose distasteful, so he sold collections of plant specimens instead, and used his spare time to study birds (Skutch 1971). Eventually, he bought a ranch in Costa Rica and with the money he makes there and through grants, he has spent his life studying the birds of Central and South America.

Skutch's (1983c) *Birds of Tropical America* is a great resource; it is filled with information on a large variety of bird species. The emphasis is on behavior, particularly mating behavior, but also foraging and care of young. For example, Skutch was the first to describe the way some birds, particularly young adults, will assist parents with the care of nestlings. A more personal view of tropical birds and of how Skutch came to know them is given in *A Bird Watcher's Adventures in Tropical America* (1977) and in *A Naturalist Amid Tropical Splendor* (1987). Skutch writes of the difficulty of travel in forest areas in South America and of the friends he made in remote regions, but most of all, he writes of birds and of the thrill of making discoveries under such trying conditions.

Skutch is now in his 90s and is still producing interesting books. He must have a huge mine of information about the birds he has observed over the years, and he continues to draw on that treasure trove in interesting ways. In 1989, he published *Birds Asleep* in which he writes that:

> studying how birds sleep may not be as exciting as watching them in full daylight ... But to know how they pass the more obscure half of their lives is necessary to round out our picture of their habits. This knowledge brings a sense of intimacy that is deeply satisfying (p. xi).

Since birds are much less obvious while sleeping, it could only be someone with the wealth of information Skutch has accumulated who could write such a book. In it, Skutch describes many behaviors including how birds conserve energy on cold nights; wrens, for example, huddle together in large groups and many birds in the high Andes sleep in rock crevices. The environment in which birds live is obviously related to bedroom choice; the blue-throated green motmot of Central America sleeps in burrows in roadside banks and in the steep, bare slopes of washouts, while sanderlings and other sandpipers often sleep on the beach balancing on one leg.

In his most recent book, Skutch focuses on a topic which is dealt with at least tangentially by anyone studying bird behavior, and that is *The Minds of Birds* (1996). In the Preface, Skutch admits that "I am far less certain of what goes on inside their heads than of what they do visibly" (p. xv). But with over 70 years of experience in observing bird behavior, Skutch is ready to set down his thoughts on what kinds of thinking birds are capable of engaging in. He realizes that he can be accused of anthropomorphism, the attribution of human characteristics to animals, but he notes that:

> when we recognize that we can hardly imagine any psychic state that we do not from time to time experience ourselves, the rigid avoidance of anthropomorphism might exclude the possibility of attributing to nonhuman animals any psychic life at all (p. xvi).

Skutch sees most bird behavior as innate, such as the woodpecker finch's use of a cactus thorn to poke into crevices in search of insects. This behavior "is an example of crystallized intelligence — a habit born of an innovative mind that no longer requires such a mind for its exercise" (p. 112). At the end of the book, Skutch writes that:

> the more profoundly and sympathetically we study birds, the stronger grows our intuition that they are conscious, until it becomes almost a certainty, and the less remote from us they appear (p. 164).

In other words, as we get to know them, there is a meeting of the minds, which makes it possible for the human mind to appreciate the bird mind. This only occurs when birds are studied "profoundly," in the fashion of Kilham and Skutch, where enough time and solitude are allowed for such communion to occur.

Another theme that has grown stronger in Skutch's later work is the importance of beauty to living things. This theme was discussed in *Life*

Ascending, but it is a major focus of *The Origin of Nature's Beauty* (1992). Skutch argues that an appreciation of beauty has an adaptive advantage. If animals were not attracted to the beauty in nature, they might be less able to withstand hardships:

> *If the azure of the sky and the verdure of the terrain were as depressing to an animal as certain drab colors can be to us, its vital processes and its will to live might be adversely affected, so that in the struggle for existence it would be less successful than some related animal who, instead of being depressed, was pleasantly excited by these widespread colors* (Skutch, 1985, p. 147).

Of course, there are also other adaptive advantages in which beauty can be seen as more than just a pleasant side benefit:

> *Much beauty in nature would never have arisen in the absence of animals with vision. Even certain of the means whereby animals escape their enemies – concealing and warning coloration – have contributed to nature's beauty. To the mutually beneficial interactions of plants with the pollinators of their flowers and dispersers of their seeds we owe much of the loveliness of vegetation. The colors and adornments of many of the most beautiful animals, above all birds, have been promoted by preferential mating* (p. xv).

But Skutch doesn't just dwell on visual beauty. It is not surprising that as an observer of birds, he also discusses the beauty of bird song, relying heavily on the work of another birdman, Charles Hartshorne. Hartshorne was a philosopher by profession, and like Kilham, was an amateur ornithologist. His *Born to Sing* (1973) is an extensive analysis of bird song, including information on the uses of song, the different types of songs, and the different singing abilities of various species. Skutch argues that:

> *no one has presented better reasons for believing that birds have aesthetic feeling, that the songs of many are music, and that they enjoy singing more than Charles Hartshorne* (p. 260).

Being a philosopher, Hartshorne is interested in analysis, in breaking a phenomenon down into its component parts, and this is what he does with bird song. Skutch approvingly cites the method Hartshorne developed for the "objective assessment of bird song" (p. 232). The six criteria of song quality are loudness; complexity; absence of interruptions; tone; organization, including rhythm, melody, and theme and variations; and imitativeness, the ability to reproduce the songs of others. This may seem like analyzing a beautiful phenomenon to death, but Hartshorne's point is that with these criteria, the different singing abilities of birds can be classified. For Skutch, the fact that some birds are much more accomplished singers than others indicates that, like other traits, this one is more highly evolved in some species than in others.

Other Birdmen

While I've focused on Kilham and Skutch, there are many other birdmen who have also written good books on the subject. There are really a great number of these, so I'll just mention the ones I've come across and particularly enjoyed. The old one is *The Charm of Birds*. I was attracted to it because its author's name is Viscount Grey of Fallodon (1927). He comes from a tradition very different from that of Kilham and Skutch. A member of the British nobility, Grey describes the birds on his estate and his experiences both observing and hunting birds. He writes of when he was first a member of Parliament in the 1890s and was forced to spend a great deal of time in London, away from his land and his birds. He became friendly with the man who took care of the waterfowl in St. James Park and visited him often "to hear news of the breeding waterfowl and to be shown various nests" (p. 182). Another birdman with political interests is Louis Halle, who wrote on the international political scene, but like Kilham, found that an interest in birds added to, rather than detracted from, his career interests. Since he traveled widely, Halle was able to observe birds in such widely different regions as India and the Alps.

Jake Page (1993), on the other hand, sticks closer to home and writes primarily of the birds he has seen near his home in the Washington, D.C. area. I bought this book because I opened to a page with the line, "Terns have always made me feel good" (p. 39). The book is filled with such observations and with a great deal of information that Page has gleaned from a variety of sources. Another writer on birds of the eastern United States is Pete Dunne, who works at the Audubon Society's Cape May Bird Observatory in New Jersey. Dunne's (1986) *Tales of a Low-Rent Birder* is less reverential than those of most of the other writers I've cited. Since Dunne is a professional, it is not surprising that he is more involved with the process of birding and the people who do it. He writes of a birdathon, a weekend event when bird watchers compete to identify the most birds. Dunne presents a very different view of birding, one that is much more communal than that of the other authors.

Though Kilham and Skutch find bird watching *en masse* distasteful, it is important to remember that for many people it is the comradery of this pastime which makes it so attractive. This is clearly the case for George

Levine (1995), whose essays in *Lifebirds* interweave thoughts on birds with thoughts on his relationships with the people who watch birds with him. For Levine, birding definitely has a social function; he deepens his relationships with people by sharing the experience of bird watching with them. Levine is an English professor and the author of *Darwin and the Novelists* (1988), but *Lifebirds* is not a work of science. While I didn't learn much about birds from this book, I found it very emotionally satisfying, and more than any other book I've read, it made me want to get out and do some bird watching myself.

Another of my favorite bird books is *My Way in Ornithology* by Olin Sewall Pettingill, Jr. (1992). Like Kilham, Pettingill developed an interest in nature early in life, spending the summers on his grandparents' farm. He went on to major in ornithology at Cornell University, and the book recounts his years as an undergraduate and then as a doctoral student there. Like Skutch, Pettingill finished his schooling during the Depression, and spent several years on various jobs and research projects which took him from Virginia to Canada. The book ends with Pettingill beginning his first academic appointment as a professor of ornithology at Carleton College in Minnesota.

Like Skutch and Kilham, Pettingill weaves together his life experiences with information on birds. I think this is what I find so attractive about their work. They are able to convey something of the emotional experience of bird watching, and I think that they are all very good at what they do because of this emotional commitment rather than in spite of it. Science is often portrayed as an endeavor in which feelings play little role because feelings can blind the scientist and ruin objectivity. While this is all true, it is only half the picture. A project will be successful only when a scientist is totally committed to it. How could these birdmen sit for untold hours in hot, humid forests or cold, wet swamps unless they were totally involved in this work both intellectually and emotionally.

What also marks the work of Kilham and Skutch is their emphasis on the individual; they are both experts at recording individual observations. Sometimes a particular behavior, once noted, is seen again and again, but some remain unique sightings. Yet these are worth mentioning too. They give a more complete picture of a species' range of behavior and make the narrative more fascinating. In each of their books, Kilham and Skutch give hundreds of facts like these, but what prevents these books from becoming mere catalogs is the way these facts are woven into stories about the birds, and about the birdmen who watch them.

References

Dunne, P. (1986). *Tales of a Low-Rent Birder.* Austin, TX: University of Texas Press.

Grey, V. (1927). *The Charm of Birds.* New York: Stokes.

Halle, L. (1989). *The Appreciation of Birds.* Baltimore, MD: Johns Hopkins University Press.

Hartsthorne, C. (1973). *Born to Sing: An Interpretation and World Survey of Bird Song.* Bloomington, IN: Indiana University Press.

Kilham, L. (1983). *Woodpeckers of Eastern North America.* New York: Dover.

Kilham, L. (1988). *On Watching Birds.* Chelsea, VT: Chelsea Green.

Kilham, L. (1989). *The American Crow and the Common Raven.* College Station, TX: Texas A&M University Press.

Levine, G. (1988). *Darwin and the Novelists.* Cambridge, MA: Harvard University Press.

Levine, G. (1995). *Lifebirds.* New Brunswick, NJ: Rutgers University Press.

O'Connell, G. (1964, May). A man of "leisure." *Dartmouth Alumni Magazine,* pp. 31-32.

Pettingill, O.S. (1992). *My Way in Ornithology.* Norman, OK: University of Oklahoma Press.

Page, J. (1993). *Songs to Birds.* Boston: Godine.

Quammen, D. (1985). *Natural Acts.* New York: Schocken.

Skutch, A. (1971). *A Naturalist in Costa Rica.* Gainesville: University Press of Florida.

Skutch, A. (1977). *A Bird Watcher's Adventures in Tropical America.* Austin, TX: University of Texas Press.

Skutch, A. (1983a). Miniatures and giants. *The Sciences, 23*(6), 18-21.

Skutch, A. (1983b). *Nature Through Tropical Windows.* Berkeley, CA: University of California Press.

Skutch, A. (1983c). *Birds of Tropical America.* Austin, TX: University of Texas Press.

Skutch, A. (1985). *Life Ascending.* Austin, TX: University of Texas Press.

Skutch, A. (1987). *A Naturalist Amid Tropical Splendor.* Iowa City, IA: University of Iowa Press.

Skutch, A. (1989). *Birds Asleep.* Austin, TX: University of Texas Press.

Skutch, A. (1992). *The Origins of Nature's Beauty.* Austin, TX: University of Texas Press.

Skutch, A. (1996). *The Minds of Birds.* College Station, TX: Texas A&M University Press.

Lungfish and Life

Several years ago, I was in a second-hand bookstore and came upon *Kamongo, or, The Lungfish and the Padre* (1932). A book with such an odd title got my attention right away, but it was the name of the author that got me to buy it. *Kamongo* was written by Homer W. Smith, a noted renal physiologist who died in 1962. I had never heard of him until I was taking graduate courses in biology at New York University in the early 1970s. Smith's name came up from time to time because he spent most of his career on the faculty of the NYU School of Medicine. When his name was used, it was with respect and with the implication that Smith had definitely added prestige to NYU (Chasis & Goldring 1965). It was also noted that he was the author of a popular book on the kidney with the intriguing title: *From Fish to Philosopher* (1953). Shortly after hearing about it, I got a paperback copy and found it to be more than I would ever want to know about the evolution of the mammalian kidney; but I did like the book because Smith's writing style was clear and direct. It was as if he were having a conversation with the reader; and I always find such a tone engaging, even when it is used to tell about the kidney.

Kamongo

It was because I had positive feelings for Smith and his writing that I bought *Kamongo,* not knowing what to expect from a book that was described on the back cover as being "part fiction and part philosophy." I am not the kind of reader who "can't put down a book" or must read a book "cover to cover in one sitting," but I did, in fact, find it difficult to stop reading *Kamongo,* and gobbled it up in two days. Smith's writing in *Fish* is good, but in *Kamongo* it's seductive. The book is essentially a dialogue between an Episcopalian priest referred to only as "the Padre" and a biologist named Joel. The conversation takes place onboard a ship that is carrying them through the Red Sea and the Suez Canal to Port Said on the Mediterranean. It is the last day of a journey during which the Padre and Joel became friendly, having sought companionship in an effort to while away the seemingly endless hours of ceaseless heat. In the first chapter, Smith describes the heat so graphically that you almost want to switch on the air conditioning; and this is what draws you into the story:

> *The walls of the ship threw their radiation against the body as though there were so little room for that all-pervading fluid in them that it must be poured with increased concentration into the haggard bodies of men and the dark spaces where they tried to hide. At the thresholds of the companionways there hung a curtain of intolerable warmth* (p.11).

It is obvious that under such conditions, there is little to do but sit on deck and talk idly. On the final day of the trip, a breeze picks up for the first time, and the relief it brings raises the travelers' spirits. Joel and the Padre now have the energy to speak of more serious things, or perhaps it is that, as they realize that they will soon be parting, each wants to discover how the other feels about issues that are important to him. The crucial conversation begins leisurely enough, befitting the venue. They talk of cigars, and Joel asks the Padre if he has such luxuries at his mission. From there each asks the other why he has been in Africa. The Padre finds it hard to put his motives into words; he sees these reasons as "the kind of thing that you grow up with, like your language; that is built into you from the very beginning" (p. 22). Joel's reasons for returning are easier to articulate: he needed more lungfish for his research. He then goes into a long and intriguing description of his efforts to find these fish during his first trip to Africa two years earlier. In this account, he tells quite a bit about the biology of lungfish, and about the climate in the part of Africa in which they are found. He also makes the search for the lungfish into a kind of detective story.

Looking for Lungfish

Joel began his quest by going to the part of Africa in which lungfish are known to live. He was interested in them because of the physiological processes that make this lifestyle possible. Lungfish live in areas where drought is common; they have adapted to this by estivating: curling in mud for years until the drought breaks, the mud mixes with water, and the lungfish can swim away. The lungfish are able to do this in part because, as their name implies, they get oxygen through lungs rather than gills. They are, in fact, related to the first animals that came to live on dry land; these animals also had lungs that served as a preadaptation to this new environment.

On reaching central Africa, Joel's first discovery was that there had just been heavy rains, the end of a long drought. With the rain went his hope of digging the fish out of the dried mud of lake beds. When he asked people where he could find lungfish, no one seemed to know what he was talking about. He recounts in detail the steps that led finally to finding a steady supply of the animals. A letter of introduction to the Director of the Natural History Museum at Nairobi didn't do him much good, but it did put him on the trail of a dentist-naturalist: "He dentisted in the morning and in the afternoon he retired, unapproachable by any pain, to a sanctuary at the rear of his house where he had built himself a laboratory" (p. 42). The dentist was familiar with the lungfish, and when he left the dentist's house Joel was "elated with success" and "full of confidence" (p. 45) that he was now on the right track. But still he couldn't find them. An engineer's information led him on a further wild-goose chase, and he finally found a lungfish, though a dead one, in the nets of local fishermen.

This brief rendition of the chase does not do it credit. Smith makes the quest intriguing and amusing with language that draws you on and on. And just when it seems that the end of the lungfish quest has come, since Joel has arranged for fishermen to bring him live specimens when they come upon them, he informs the Padre that this led to still another problem: he couldn't keep the fish alive. Fishermen would bring him live lungfish in buckets and tubs, and within a few hours the fish would be dead. Nothing he fed them or did to the water seemed to matter. He implies that he was very stupid not to see the real cause of the problem, but he keeps the Padre — and the reader — in suspense as to what the problem was, as he continues with the tale of his misadventures.

Joel's dilemma was finally solved when a native chief brought him a lungfish in a bucket. When Joel went to look at it, it was dead, and all of sudden he realized why:

> *The fish had drowned, of course! They had drowned in the fishermen's nets, in the shallow tubs, they had drowned. ... as a matter of fact, they cannot live beneath the water for more than a few hours. Their gills are greatly reduced in size, almost vestigial, and even in the water they rise to the surface every fifteen minutes or so to fill their lungs with air* (p. 61).

With the mystery solved, Joel still had to find a reliable supply of the fish, and this came from a rather unlikely source. A prison warden brought him to a lakeshore where a work gang of prisoners was clearing papyrus from the banks. There the warden showed him a bucket with a half-dozen live lungfish in it "kicking around as happy as larks" (p. 64). The warden explained that the fish fell out of papyrus roots dragged onto the shore; the inmates usually saved the fish for dinner, but Joel was free to take some since he seemed so pleased with the sight of them.

Dead Ends

After these problems, Joel has a successful period of research in Africa, so successful that he returns to collect more lungfish to bring back to the United States. But talk of the success of his work brings him to the subject of the lack of evolutionary success of the lungfish, and thus to the heart of the book. Joel notes that when the lungfish ...

> *dived into the mud he dived into a blind alley, into a mode of life that must ultimately end in extinction. The proof of this lies in the fact that he is nearing that end. The marvel is that he has survived this long* (p. 67).

In other words, the lungfish is an evolutionary dead end. Though it is related to the animals that first came on dry land, its lineage developed in a different direction — adapted to a different lifestyle, one that led to a specialization that prohibited much innovation. The lungfish is a remnant, a living fossil.

The idea of an organism being a dead end upsets the Padre; he suffers "perplexity over a Nature that could play such scurvy tricks" (p. 81). The Padre sees everything in nature as having a purpose, and an organism that seems futile is offensive to that vision. For the rest of the book, Joel and the Padre wrestle with this problem, as Joel gives examples of the purposelessness of nature. The Padre counters, not so much with evidence in opposition, but with arguments for why nature can't really be this way.

In a beautiful passage that is similar to Edward O. Wilson's description of a tropical forest in *Biophilia* (1984), Joel describes the rich abundance of life associated with a single tree in a rain forest. He sees no rhyme or reason to this life, no order to this chaos. But here again, the Padre counters: How can the order of life arise from simple chaos, mustn't there be some Being organizing the world? Joel argues against this idea in a passage which, though written in the 1930s, is very reminiscent of some of the recent work on chaos and complexity theory. Joel sees life as a whirlpool organized out of the chaos of moving water. One does not need to posit the existence of a supernatural being to explain the development of a whirl, and thus, life, too, can be seen as arising out of chaos. A whirlpool, if perturbed, splits into two, and can be compared to the expansion of life on Earth. This simple description does not do justice to the extended metaphor that Smith develops in the chapter that is at the heart of the book. This discussion ends as the ship pulls into port, and the disturbed Padre asks: If there is no Supreme Being does this mean there is no purpose to life? Joel answers that life "has no purpose except as you choose to give it one" (p. 150).

I'll return to this idea, which was an important one in Smith's thought, but I want to note here that though *Kamongo* deals with important philosophical and religious questions, there is also quite a bit of biology in it. Smith manages to effortlessly present many important ideas on evolution, on the richness of tropical life, and on the adaptations of the lungfish. But though Smith used lungfish in his work in order to better understand kidney function, there is nothing here on kidney research. And despite the biology it does contain, *Kamongo* is not so much a work of popularization of science as a philosophical discourse that is written in the language of the layperson. It was 20 years before Smith published a book on the kidney for the general reader. In the meantime, he published two textbooks on renal physiology (1937, 1951), as well as another novel and a book on religion.

The End of Illusion

The novel is *The End of Illusion* (1935) and it is set in Malay, another area where Smith went in search of lungfish. But fish play no role in this book, and neither does science, though the major theme in *Kamongo* — what is the meaning of life — is also central here. This time the theme is treated in the form of what amounts to a mystery story: Did an engineer die in an accidental fall at a building site, or did he fall to his death during a fight with the manager of the project as a result of a rivalry over, of course, a woman? I think this is quite a good novel. It has the same rich descriptive language that *Kamongo* has, and Smith again creates a rich atmosphere that is easily imagined by the reader. But while *Kamongo* was a critical and monetary success, *The End of Illusion* wasn't. Smith became so discouraged that he never attempted another novel. I think this is a shame because he was quite good at writing fiction. While reading *Kamongo,* I was amazed that someone who was so successful as a biologist could have had the mental energy to create such beautiful and meaningful prose.

Man and His Gods

In giving up writing novels, Smith did not give up writing for the public. In the same year that *The End of Illusion* was published, he started work on a book that took him almost 20 years to complete. *Man and His Gods* (1952) is a history of religion, or rather a history of Smith's view that Western religion became supplanted by science over the centuries. Smith begins with the evolution of humans and their early religions, and then goes on to examine the Egyptian, Babylonian, Hebrew, Greek, Roman and Christian religions. His aim is to show that the need for the invocation of supernatural forces to explain phenomena and events became less and less important as these could be explained by science. He also tries to show that the gods of the various religions can be traced to historical figures; that religion is the invention of human minds working on the events that they see occurring around them. Here, as in his two novels, Smith sets forth arguments for the idea that humans are responsible for what happens in their lives, and that:

> the only truths that man could trust were those of correspondence discoverable by the mind, and these must be held constantly subject to revision. The only certitude was that man was an animal struggling to live in a world from which had faded the last faint ray of transcendental light (p. 438).

This quote comes at the end of the book's last chapter. This chapter is followed by a section called "The Story of This Book," which is the only autobiographical material Smith ever published. It tells of his early life and of how he became interested in science and in questioning the meaning of life. When he was about nine years old, he received a chemistry book as a Christmas gift and immediately became fascinated with this science. Later, while Smith was recovering from a bad case of the measles, his father built him a shack in the backyard. (His mother died when he was seven.) There he could continue his experiments while the family would be left in peace. Smith tells with relish of not only the chemistry he did there, but of the gadgets he built, and of the dissections he did under the direction of his sister's fiancé, a medical student. Things continued in this way until he was 17 years old. When he read the headlines about the sinking of the *Titanic*, he was struck by how prominently the papers reported that the ship's band played "Nearer, My God, to Thee" as the ship went down. He found this disturbing, not so much because this was what the band did, but because the newspapers made so much of it. It got him thinking and he writes:

> *I wrestled, in my own terms, with the Meaning of Things. I took a sharp scalpel and took the wrappings off life and took a close look at its insides. ... On that April 15, 1912, this book was begun* (p. 474).

And in a sense, *Kamongo* and *The End of Illusion* were also begun on that day. Smith spent his life grappling with the question of life's meaning; when he gave up writing novels, the question stuck with him, and he attempted to deal with it in *Man and His Gods*.

From Fish to Philosopher

There is even a hint of this grappling in *From Fish to Philosopher*. The title itself is rather peculiar for a book on the kidney. The "fish" makes sense because one of the major functions of the kidney is to control water and salt levels in the blood, a problem that is very different for a fish than for a land animal. But "philosopher" is another study; what could the kidney possibly have to do with philosophy? Smith's answer, and the reason for the title, is that the complex kidney found in mammals was necessary for the evolution of the human brain. This kidney provides for the precise control of blood composition, something essential for the proper functioning of the brain.

To develop his "philosopher" theme, Smith devotes the last chapter of the book to an examination of consciousness. This is an odd chapter to include in a book on the kidney, but his philosopher theme gives him an excuse to deal with the same problem he dealt with in his other books for a general audience; how to explain the mysteries of life, including the mystery of human consciousness, without resorting to the supernatural. He works to show that consciousness is the result of cellular activities not very different from the activities of cells in even the simplest organisms. And to show the powers of the mind, he devotes several pages to how the brain functions below the level of consciousness after one has learned a complex task. The task Smith uses as an example is playing the piano. Not coincidentally, he was an excellent pianist and also a composer; but what he focuses on here is how many notes a pianist can play in a second. He discusses particularly difficult pieces of music, and the rate at which especially accomplished pianists can play the notes in these pieces. His point is to show that, while a beginning pianist is conscious of every note and thus plays each slowly, an expert pianist's skill involves note playing that does not directly involve the conscious mind. I think the reason he included this discussion in *Fish* was because he found the topic so intriguing and couldn't resist including it.

From *Fish to Philosopher* is an unusual book, but definitely worth reading. Smith's ideas on the origin of the first terrestrial animals are somewhat dated. But his emphasis on the importance of geological history to biological history, his discussion of kidney function in various animal groups, and his interesting asides about research on the kidney in various species, all contribute to making this book noteworthy. While it was written as a science popularization for the general reader, I'm not sure many nonbiologists would ever finish it. *Fish* is much more technical than Smith's other books for the general reader, but it is easily accessible to the biologist. In fact, it could be argued, at least by biology teachers, that there is a need for more books like Smith's: books that are clearly written and interesting, but that have more scientific information and go into more depth than the average popularization does. Such books would synthesize original research, material that we don't have the time or the expertise to sift through, and present it in an understandable form along with interesting pieces of information and stories that we can use to enliven our classes. Smith's description of how he managed to get cut-off oil barrels, each with a live lungfish inside, back to the United States safely, and with two-thirds of the fish still alive, is one example of the kind of story I'm talking about.

Rambling

This column seems to have been a particularly rambling one, and one without a great deal of information. Maybe this is because it is for the first issue of the school year, and I don't want to leave the languor of summer just yet. Or maybe it's because I think it's a good idea to leave the facts of biology once in awhile and examine the motivations and interests of those who do biology. I chose to write about Homer W. Smith because I found *Kamongo* to be such a beautiful book that I wanted to share it. Also, I was so surprised by Smith's skill as a writer that it reminded me once again about something that's easy to forget as we read about researchers and tell our students about them: that biologists are at least as multidimensional as are the rest of the population. Yes, Smith was a brilliant physiologist, but he was also a novelist, historian, pianist, composer, and, perhaps most importantly, a teacher. We all reflect on the meaning of life from time to time, usually considering this issue separately from our interests in science. But

Smith reminds us that all the parts of our lives are interrelated – they enrich and shed light on each other – and this seems a particularly good thought with which to start a new school year.

References

Chasis, H. & Goldring, W. (Eds.). (1965). *Homer William Smith: His Scientific and Literary Achievements.* New York: New York University Press.

Smith, H.W. (1932). *Kamongo, or, The Lungfish and the Padre.* New York: Viking.

Smith, H.W. (1935). *The End of Illusion.* New York: Harper.

Smith, H.W. (1937). *The Physiology of the Kidney.* New York: Oxford University Press.

Smith, H.W. (1951). *The Kidney; Structure and Function in Health and Disease.* New York: Oxford University Press.

Smith, H.W. (1952). *Man and His Gods.* Boston: Little, Brown.

Smith, H.W. (1953). *From Fish to Philosopher.* Boston: Little, Brown.

Wilson, E.O (1984). *Biophilia.* Cambridge, MA: Harvard University Press.

Learning to Read
in Poughkeepsie

I am writing this column at Vassar College in Poughkeepsie, New York, which is about a two-hour drive from our home on Long Island, but I feel as if I am in a foreign country. I am staying in a dorm, itself a disconcerting experience, and I am a participant in a six-week Summer Institute sponsored by the National Endowment for the Humanities. The title of the Institute is "The Environmental Imagination," and it is a tour through American nature writing taught by a team of scholars in the field, including Lawrence Buell (1995) of Harvard University who wrote the book after which the Institute is titled. The Institute is directed by H. Daniel Peck, author of a great book on Thoreau (1990), and one of the most patient men in the world (I think an institute director has to be). I'm one of 25 participants in the Institute, all college faculty, the majority of whom teach literature, but there are other disciplines represented, including geography, philosophy, theology and art history. I am the lone biologist in the group, so I am definitely out of my element here, and this has contributed to the excitement and the exhaustion I feel about this experience.

While I am the only one here designated as a biologist, there are actually many members of the group who are quite knowledgeable about many areas of biology, which is not surprising considering the topic of the Institute. During the first week, the group sorted itself into several subgroups including the fly fishers, the bird-watchers, and the gardeners. We have had very few free hours, but these groups managed to avidly pursue their interests, and they added to their numbers as the weeks went by. For many of the participants, love of nature and love of nature writing are closely intertwined. Their experiences in nature allow them to read the literature with greater understanding, and the literature provides insights that deepen their appreciation of nature.

We are now in the final week of the Institute, and are hurrying to read and learn as much as we can before heading home. As someone outside the field of literature, I've had to work particularly hard to keep up with the reading, so I haven't had much time to really consider what this experience means to me. Since this column is due next week, I have decided to sit down and give you my first impressions while the events are still fresh in my mind, but with the warning that a number of future columns will also deal with aspects of the Institute. This experience has been so rich that it will affect my writing, my teaching, and my thinking for years to come.

Reading Poetry

The first day of the Institute was an exciting and rather frightening experience for me. I had read all the assigned readings for the week before I arrived at Vassar. I thought I was ready for week one, though I wasn't so prepared for the other weeks. But on that first day we looked at the work of the colonial New England poet, Anne Bradstreet (Hensley 1967), and I knew I was in trouble. The faculty for the week, Elisa New and John Elder, found themes in the poems such as the links between the everyday and the eternal, between here and heaven, that had completely escaped me. I had read the poems and had understood what they were about: In "A Letter to Her Husband, Absent upon Public Employment," Bradstreet writes of how she misses her husband when he has traveled to England; "In Memory of Anne" is a lament for her dead grandchild. But during the discussion, I discovered there was a lot more going on in these poems. Some of the more astute readers in the group pointed out that Bradstreet's language indicated her attitude toward God, toward the wilderness around her, and toward her role as a woman in a new world. The discussion reminded me of discussions in the literature course I took in college 30 years ago; I had found it fascinating that there was so much more meaning in a poem than was readily apparent to my untutored mind. But 30 years ago, I was so immersed in becoming a scientist that I pursued literature no further. Now I was being reeducated. The process of revealing layers and layers within texts continued day after day. I was learning to read all over again, learning to read in a whole new way. Or perhaps it would be better to say that I was learning to ask many new questions about a text.

Text and Frame

"Text" is a word that literature people use a lot. They are always referring to "the text." And after a couple of weeks of this, I finally discovered why. It relates to a type of literacy criticism, the school that sees the text, the words on the page, as the important thing; the life of the author, the culture of the time, and the historical context of the work should all be ignored. While we didn't always do this, the frequent use of the term text was an indication that the words on the page were central to every discussion. Another term that I found the literature people using frequently was "frame." They were always framing an argument or shifting a frame, and I came to understand that what they meant by framing a discussion was presenting what they saw as the important aspects of the text to focus upon. Framing was a way of organizing or directing discussion. But why am I going into all of this here, in a journal for biology teachers? What do biologists care about texts and frames, things that seem to be better left to teachers of literature? Or should they? Maybe these are things that we, too, should pay some attention to. The more I think about it, the more I see framing a discussion as a very good thing for me to do in class; it may be good to give students some idea of where we are headed, of what I think may be some items worthy of attention in discussion.

I think close attention to text can also mean something for a biologist. At Vassar, I came to realize that in the past I had paid close attention to texts, but in a very specific way. When I read William Bartram's (1791) *Travels* or Henry David Thoreau's (1854) *Walden,* I read them for what they could tell me about the living world, what biological observations these writers had made that were interesting or useful to me. My frame had been a very small one; I had only asked one question of the text. But those in literature have asked many questions, such as how did the fact that William Bartram wrote during the Revolutionary War influence his writing, and how did Thoreau's interest in Emerson's transcendentalism affect his work. In everything we read, it was apparent that human observation of the living world is always done within a particular cultural context, and this was a very interesting thing for me to realize. I don't think I will ever read anything, including research articles and biology textbooks, in quite the same way again. It can be exhausting to be so analytical, but the payoff in terms of an enriched understanding of "the text" is definitely worth it. There is a whole field devoted to such analysis of scientific texts; it's called the rhetoric of science and it deals with how language is used in scientific writing to inform and convince. If you are interested in this area, two good books in the field are Charles Bazerman's (1988) *Shaping Written Knowledge* and *Understanding Scientific Prose* (Selzer 1993), a collection of papers that all analyze one scientific paper.

New and Old Writers

At Vassar I discovered both nature writers who were completely new to me and new aspects of writers with whom I was long familiar. One of my favorite "new" writers is Josephine Johnson (1969) who wrote *An Inland Island* about the 37 farmland acres in Ohio that she and her husband were allowing to become wild again. Johnson is a careful observer of nature and a writer of vivid descriptions; she also interweaves her observations with discussions of environmental and political issues. Another writer who was new to me is Celia Thaxter, who wrote two books about her life on Mount Desert Island off the coast of Maine: *Among the Isles of Shoals* (1888) and *An Island Garden* (1894). The latter is about the beautiful garden that she created and that was painted by several American impressionist artists who visited the island, most notably Childe Hassam.

Johnson and Thaxter were two of the writers of the Institute that was devoted to women nature writers. The two faculty for the week, Carolyn Merchant and Vera Norwood, have themselves made important contributions to the environmental literature. Merchant has written several books (1979, 1996) in which she argues that the "dominant narrative," the story which underlies our view of nature, is one that is masculine in perspective and perceives nature as something to be controlled and mastered. She sees the need for a new narrative, one that has a feminine as well as a masculine aspect, and that involves a human partnership with nature. In *Made from This Earth: American Women and Nature,* Vera Norwood (1993) also takes on the dominant narrative, but from a different perspective. She looks at how American women viewed nature and wrote about it. She discusses Thaxter, Johnson, and a host of other women, including women botanists such as Kate Sessions and Alice Eastwood, and women artists such as Leta Hughley and Deborah Passmore, who documented American plants and animals in illustrations for publications with texts that were often written by male biologists.

In week three of the Institute, the writers we discussed had long been familiar to me: John Burroughs and John Muir. Lawrence Buell, who served as a faculty member for four weeks of the Institute, and Frank Bergon, who is a Burroughs scholar, led us in a number of lively discussions. Bergon started the week with a presentation on Burrough's life and work. Burroughs (1981, 1992) lived not far from Vassar and most of his writings deal with the area around his home. He is a writer of domestic nature, who was especially interested in observing the bird life he encountered on his wanderings near home. Muir (1911, 1918), on the other hand, was a proponent of the wilderness. Though he was born on a farm in Wisconsin, he traveled west as a young man, and most of his writings are about the West. In a rather odd essay called "Wild Wool" which was published in *Steep Trails* (1918), Muir extols the virtues of the wool of wild sheep in comparison to that of domestic sheep. For Muir, wildness is good and domestication is bad, not only in terms of the land itself, but in terms of animals as well. He was an early conservationist and a founder of the Sierra Club. Burroughs was less strident in his environmentalism, but as Bergon pointed out, Burroughs was well aware of the dangers that development posed to the plants and animals he treasured. Treating Muir and Burroughs, who were contemporaries, in the same week highlighted how writers' presentations of nature can be very different, and how attitudes toward protecting nature are also varied.

One of the things that became clear during the Institute was that there are no easy answers to environmental problems, and that even defining an environmental problem is difficult. The book *Uncommon Ground: Rethinking the Human Place in Nature* (Cronon 1995) treats just these issues. It is a collection of essays dealing with many varieties of human relationship with nature. The volume's editor, William Cronon, writes in an essay on "The Trouble with Wilderness" that often too much emphasis is placed on the preservation of wilderness areas while other environments are given less attention. He traces our present-day idea of wilderness back to the 18th century where wild nature was thought of as sublime and powerful. His "principle objection to wilderness is that it may teach us to be dismissive or even contemptuous of such humble places and experiences" as our own backyards and "of the nature that is all around us if only we have eyes to see it" (p. 86). Other essays in the volume deal with everything from the nature to be found in the Nature Company to the relationship of environmental issues to issues of social justice.

Field Trips

The Institute involved more than just discussion of environmental literature. There were evening programs, including a concert on music and nature and a film series. These were in addition to the seminars in the morning, and then one afternoon a week we had a field trip. We made two visits to the Mohonk Preserve, first to study the geology of the area and then to study the chemistry of the area's lakes. The Mohonk Preserve is adjacent to the Mohonk Mountain House, a resort that was originally founded by Albert and Alfred Smiley in 1969 and is still run by the Smiley family. The Smiley family established the Mohonk Preserve on much of the land surrounding the Mountain House. The Smiley family has also made other significant contributions to the protection of the environment through the person of Daniel Smiley, the grandnephew of the founders. Born in 1907, Dan Smiley lived most of his life at Mohonk and worked at the resort in a number of capacities involving both business and recreation operations, but his real interest was in learning more about the natural history of the area (Burgess 1996).

From 1938 until his death in 1989, Dan Smiley ran the Mohonk Weather Station, keeping daily records on the temperature, precipitation, and other weather phenomena. He regularly checked the acid level of Lake Mohonk, something he had begun doing in 1931, when an acid testing kit came with a new refrigeration system. Smiley was also interested in the living world, banding more than 17,000 birds and keeping meticulous records on the growth of trees and other vegetation, often correlating such observations with weather data. All this information is invaluable and has been preserved in the Daniel Smiley Research Center at the Mohonk Preserve, where the botanist, Paul Huth, serves as Director of Research. Huth began working with Smiley in 1974, so he has an appreciation for the man and for the value of the data Smiley accumulated. Huth oversees an active research program at the Center where work is done on analyzing Smiley's data and adding to it (Huyghe 1991).

Another field trip was to the Vassar Ecological Preserve that is adjacent to the campus. This is farmland that is now being allowed to become reforested. We collected insects, brought them back to the Field Station at the Preserve where we identified the insects, and determined their relative abundance in the samples. It was nice to see professors of literature coming to understand the significance of the idea that the most common insect species are rare and the rarest are most common, meaning that only a few insect species are present in large numbers, but a large number of species are present in small numbers. Last week, we studied plant reproduction in

Vassar's Shakespeare Garden, where the plants mentioned in Shakespeare's writings are displayed. This garden is only a small part of Vassar's beautiful campus, which covers a large area, with room for two lakes, two streams, and a golf course. The campus itself is an arboretum with an extensive collection of tree species — more than 200 species — and many beautiful old specimens. There is an immense purple beech that I pass everyday on my way to class, making it difficult to leave the outdoors.

A Sense of Place

Though I am anxious to leave my dorm room when the Institute ends and to get home to my husband, Vassar is a beautiful place, and I'm going to regret leaving it. A sense of place was one of the issues that came up many times during the Institute. Many nature writers focus on a particular place in their work. For Thoreau, it was primarily the environs of Concord; for Mary Austin (1903) who wrote *Land of Little Rain*, it was the deserts of California; for Wendell Berry (1981) it is his farm in Kentucky. Several times our discussions came around to our own sense of place. Laurie Kutchins (1993), a poet, spoke of being torn between her love for the dry lands of her native Wyoming and her present home in the hills of Virginia near James Madison University, where she teaches. Other participants told of similar displacements, and this got me thinking about the whole issue of human habitat. Biologists are very aware of the habitat requirements of the plants and animals they study, but they may be less aware of what members of their own species require. Our discussions made me more aware of my sense of place, something I had totally taken for granted. I've discovered that I need trees. A landscape devoid of them seems forbidding to me; trees mean comfort.

Talk of a sense of place led to discussion of the mental maps we carry around with us. This is a topic that Barry Lopez focuses on in "The Country of the Mind," a chapter of *Arctic Dreams* (1986). Lopez was a writer I had heard of, but had never read before the Institute. As with any educational experience, this one forced me to do things that I was not able to do on my own, and reading Lopez is something that I'm very glad I had to do. His writing is mesmerizing; his insights and the way he presents them are intriguing. In "The Country of the Mind," he writes of Pingok Island off the north coast of Alaska and of the different perceptions, different mental maps, of the island that are created in the minds of those who live on the island, both animal and human inhabitants, and of those who visit it. He also writes of what goes into creating such maps, and how not only humans but animals must use such constructs to navigate around the "local landscape" that is familiar to them. Thus there is a host of different ways of experiencing a landscape, of developing a sense of place.

Visiting Writers

Barry Lopez was one of four writers who participated in the Institute. Each writer would give a reading on a Thursday night, and then join the Friday seminar for a discussion of his or her work. The other three writers were A.R. Ammons, Terry Tempest Williams, and Linda Hogan. We were assigned to read at least one work by each author so that we would be prepared for the seminar. Ammons is a poet; I had read his book *The Selected Poems* (1986) and his *Sumerian Vistas* (1987), but I must admit that he wasn't one of my favorite poets. His idea of nature was too physical to me; he seemed more interested in water and rocks than in living things. But then he came to speak to us, and my idea of his work changed radically. Unlike most of the other participants, several of whom are poets themselves, I had never been to a poetry reading before. In fact, I had never heard a writer read her or his own work. Such things just aren't done in science; someone may report on the research published in a journal article, but he or she usually doesn't read the article. Words, the way of saying something, the text, just aren't as important in science as in literature. Poetry is different, and for the first time I realized that poetry is meant to be read out loud. The phrasing, the inflection, the pace with which Ammons read, made his poetry come alive for me. I suddenly realized that his work was about nature in a very deep sense, and I came away from the reading and the next day's seminar with a much greater appreciation for his work.

I also looked at Lopez's work differently after his visit to the Institute, and the same was true of Terry Tempest Williams' writing. Last year I had read Williams' *Pieces of White Shell* (1984) which is about the land of the Navahoes, and for the Institute, I read both *Refuge* (1991), in which the story of her mother's death from cancer is interwoven with the story of the exceptional rise of the Great Salt Lake in the 1980s, and *An Unspoken Hunger* (1994), a collection of essays. Williams writes very well, but her work comes to life even more when she reads it, and I think most of the participants would agree that her presence at the seminar was an extremely moving occasion. She got us talking about ourselves, and generously listened to us as much as we listened to her.

Linda Hogan is arriving later this week, and I am looking forward to her visit. I enjoyed *Dwellings* (1995), her book of essays, so much that I also read her novel *Solar Storms* (1995), which is about the struggle of Indian women in northern Minnesota to save the land from environmental destruction. This description hardly does the novel justice; Hogan writes beautifully and with a sense of human courage that is wonderful to experience. And I think "experience" is the right word here; you don't just read *Solar Storms,* you experience it. *Dwellings* is also a wonderful book. In these essays, Hogan interweaves Indian stories and beliefs with observations on the living world, biological information, and spiritual meditations. There is an essay on bats that is great, and another that includes a description of a porcupine — both alive and then dead — that is memorable.

This word could also be used to describe a short story by Ursula LeGuin that we read, and that I have to mention because of two paragraphs I love so much. The story is called "Schrödinger's Cat" and it's in the collection *Buffalo Gals and Other Animal Presences* (1974). Not surprisingly, it's about a cat that is hard to pin down, as is the hypothetical cat in the physicist Schrödinger's thought experiment about a cat in charge of moving atoms from one compartment to another. We read the story because it says something about the difficulty of pinning down nature and about the idea of chaos that is so important to both postmodern literature and science. But I liked the story for what it says about living things. In a couple of paragraphs LeGuin reveals a great deal about the essence of life. She writes of the "metabolic frenzy" of the hummingbird, and of swallows cracking "the sound barrier." Most unforgettably, she writes that "worms shot like subway trains through the dirt of gardens, among the writhing roots of roses" (p. 161). As a New Yorker, I think this is a great sentence and one I'll long remember.

Leaving Vassar

When I drive home from Vassar, I will be physically exhausted from six hectic weeks of literature and nature, talking and listening. My head will be spinning with new ways of reading and appreciating literature, new ways of looking at the natural world, and new ways of thinking about environmental problems. I will return to teaching with a greater respect for "texts," for the meaning of words on a page, and I'll try to bring my students to a greater appreciation of the written word. I'll also return more willing to collaborate with my colleagues who teach English on ways to present nature writing to students and to encourage students to write about their experiences in the natural world. And finally, I'll return with a desire to read all the nature writing I can get my hands on. What could be better than reading about the living world that I have taught about for so many years?

Acknowledgment

The research for this article was done during the 1997 National Endowment for the Humanities Summer Institute, "The Environmental Imagination" at Vassar College. I would like to especially thank Dan Peck, who directed the Institute, as well as Ina Bennett, Rachel Azima, and Lucas Smith. They all worked very hard to make the Institute memorable for the participants, and I am very grateful to them for the wonderful time I had in Poughkeepsie.

References

Ammons, A.R. (1986). *The Selected Poems*. New York: Norton.

Ammons, A.R. (1987). *Sumerian Vistas*. New York: Norton.

Austin, M. (1903). *Land of Little Rain*. Boston: Houghton Mifflin.

Bartram, W. (1791). *Travels*. Salt Lake City, UT: Peregrine Smith (1980 edition).

Bazerman, C. (1988). *Shaping Written Knowledge: The Genre and Activity of the Experimental Article in Science*. Madison, WI: University of Wisconsin Press.

Berry, W. (1981). *Recollected Essays 1965-1980*. San Francisco: North Point.

Buell, L. (1995). *The Environmental Imagination: Thoreau, Nature Writing, and the Formation of American Culture*. Cambridge, MA: Harvard University Press.

Burgess, L. (1996). *Daniel Smiley of Mohonk: A Naturalist's Life*. Fleischmanns, NY: Purple Mountain.

Burroughs, J. (1981). *Signs and Seasons*. New York: Harper's.

Burroughs, J. (1992). *Birch Browsings*. New York: Penguin.

Cronon, W. (Ed.). (1995). *Uncommon Ground: Rethinking the Human Place in Nature*. New York: Norton.

Hensley, J. (Ed.). (1967). *The Works of Anne Bradstreet*. Cambridge, MA: Harvard University Press.

Hogan, L. (1995). *Dwellings: A Spiritual History of the Natural World*. New York: Norton.

Hogan, L. (1995). *Solar Storms*. New York: Scribner.

Huyghe, P. (1991, July/August). A naturalist preserved. *The Sciences*, pp. 12-15.

Johnson, J. (1969). *An Inland Island*. New York: Simon & Schuster.

Kutchins, L. (1993). *Between Towns*. Lubbock, TX: Texas Tech University Press.

LeGuin, U. (1974). *Buffalo Gals and Other Animal Presences*. Santa Barbara, CA: Capra.

Lopez, B. (1986). *Arctic Dreams: Imagination and Desire in a Northern Landscape*. New York: Scribner's.

Merchant, C. (1979). *The Death of Nature: Women, Ecology, and the Scientific Revolution*. San Francisco: Harper & Row.

Merchant, C. (1996). *Earthcare: Women and the Environment.* New York: Routledge.

Muir, J. (1911). *My First Summer in the Sierra.* Boston: Houghton Mifflin.

Muir, J. (1918). *Steep Trails.* Boston: Houghton Mifflin.

Norwood, V. (1993). *Made from This Earth: American Women and Nature.* Chapel Hill, NC: University of North Carolina Press.

Peck, H.D. (1990). *Thoreau's Morning Work: Memory and Perception in* A Week on the Concord and Merrimack Rivers, the Journal, and Walden. New Haven, CT: Yale University Press.

Selzer, J.(Ed.). (1993). *Understanding Scientific Prose.* Madison, WI: University of Wisconsin Press.

Thaxter, C. (1888). *Among the Isles of Shoals.* Boston: Houghton Mifflin.

Thaxter, C. (1894). *An Island Garden.* Boston: Houghton Mifflin.

Thoreau, H.D. (1854). *Walden.* New York: Harper's (1950 edition).

Williams, T.T. (1984). *Pieces of White Shell.* New York: Scribner's.

Williams, T.T. (1991). *Refuge: An Unnatural History of Family and Place.* New York: Pantheon.

Williams, T.T. (1994). *An Unspoken Hunger.* New York: Pantheon.

Aldo Leopold Reconsidered

The first time I read Aldo Leopold's *A Sand County Almanac* (1949) I didn't think much of it. I hesitate to admit this incredible lack of insight, but apparently this was a rather common reaction at the time the book was published. In fact, it wasn't until the 1970s that the book was given the attention and critical evaluation it deserved. I myself changed my opinion when I reread it several years ago. I was induced to do this after coming across an article by George Vukelich (1987), "Secret of the Diseased Trees," which tells of how Leopold valued the rotting trees in his woodlot. Leopold wrote of his woodlot in the *Sand Country* essay called "A Mighty Fortress," which is now one of my favorites, one I often assign to my students. In it, Leopold notes that many animals find diseased trees very useful: wild bees build combs in hollow oaks and grouse eat oak galls and find winter protection among the branches of oak windfalls.

Conservation Esthetic

I enjoyed this essay so much that I reread the whole book and completely changed my opinion of it; *A Sand County Almanac* is a gem of beautiful writing with wonderful ideas on ecology and environmental issues. For me, the most memorable essay is "Conservation Esthetic," in which Leopold outlines the pleasures people experience in natural settings. I reread this in 1991, a year after finishing my doctoral dissertation on the aesthetic of biology. I had really missed the boat in not including Leopold because in this essay he considers something that few people do in discussing the aesthetic experience of nature: that this experience can be very different for different people, that it is hardly the same experience for all. He describes five different reasons people go to nature for pleasure and focuses on how the varied motivations affect the land. The first reason is to acquire a "trophy": to hunt deer or ducks, to fish, to take photographs, to collect sea shells, etc. While taking pictures doesn't usually damage a natural setting, hunting or fishing can, so trophy collection can be problematic. The next reason is to seek solitude and a feeling of oneness with nature, and here again, too many people obviously can destroy the pleasure. But Leopold contends that for the third reason, getting fresh air and a change of scene, "mass-use neither destroys nor dilutes this value" (p. 172). While I might dispute this point, it is true that the thousands of people who jam Long Island's Jones Beach on a Saturday in July are all enjoying the sun, the sand and the ocean.

The last two pleasures to be derived from contact with nature are more sophisticated. Leopold's fourth pleasure is in nature study, in perceiving "the natural processes by which the land and the living things upon it have achieved their characteristic forms (evolution) and by which they maintain their existence (ecology)" (p.173). In other words, there is pleasure to be found in observing nature and learning about it. Here again, this activity does not "use up" nature; any number can be involved. Finally, there is pleasure in husbanding nature, in working to protect it from degradation, "when some art of management is applied to land by some person of perception" (p. 175).

I find this analysis of the conservation aesthetic very powerful. Here is someone who has thought about the reasons why people seek contact with nature, and has considered the varied consequences of that contact. This is a much more perceptive approach to the aesthetic of nature than the usual: nature is beautiful – period. At the end of this analysis Leopold hints that these five approaches can be seen as steps in a deepening relationship with nature, that the "trophy-recreationist" consumes resources which those who study nature and husband it do not. So Leopold is doing more here than analyzing why people go to nature; he is pleading for a particular kind of relationship with nature, a relationship of respect and valuing. In fact, his whole book can be seen as pleading this cause.

A Sand County Almanac

Leopold had a hard time getting *A Sand County Almanac* published. For several years, he worked with editors at Knopf to mold the essays he had written into a book, until finally Knopf flatly rejected the manuscript.

At this point, he reworked some of the pieces, added others, and came up with the three-part form in which the book was finally published by Oxford University Press. Leopold died of a heart attack a week after the manuscript was accepted for publication; this happened 50 years ago this spring, on April 21, 1948. It was after his death that the book was given its title, though few other changes were made to the manuscript. Some critics think that if Leopold had lived, he would have made further revisions, but Paul Fritzell (1990) contends that the book's form is very effective as it stands, with the three parts serving different roles while remaining closely related to each other.

The first section is the almanac. Composed of essays for each month of the year, it contains the observations Leopold made at the abandoned farm he bought in the lowland country of central Wisconsin. The second part is made up of essays about Leopold's more far-flung experiences with nature, including notes on his years working for the U.S. Forest Service in the Southwest early in his career, before he became a professor of wildlife management at the University of Wisconsin at Madison. The final section, which includes "Conservation Esthetic," is called "The Upshot" and deals with basic issues of land use and preservation.

While *Sand County* can be seen as a progression from the particular to the general and from the descriptive to the theoretical, the book is really more complexly structured than that. To me, the first section is much more than simply descriptions of what Leopold observed on his land. There is quite a bit of ecology and of deduction from observation here. Leopold manages to say a great deal, but in such an agreeable way that the reader is almost unaware of how much is being presented. Read only one of these entries carefully and you will be amazed at how much he manages to slip in. For example, in an essay called "Prairie Birthday" he begins by noting that many people are unaware of when the wild plants they pass by, or even step on, bloom:

> *Tell me of what plant-birthday a man takes notice, and I shall tell you a good deal about his vocation, his hobbies, his hay fever, and the general level of his ecological education* (p. 44).

Silphium

Leopold then goes on to discuss one remnant of the original prairie, a plant called Silphium, that he has come upon in a corner of a country graveyard where the mower fails to reach:

What a thousand acres of Silphiums looked like when they tickled the bellies of the buffalo is a question never again to be answered, and perhaps not even asked (p. 45).

Leopold goes into the biology of Silphium, drawing on ideas from botany and ecology to explain why it was able to survive fire and grazing by buffalo, and why it was edging toward extinction under intensive cattle grazing. In a few pages, he has given not only a great deal of information about this plant, but about the ecology of the prairie and human disturbance of nature.

It is difficult to find an essay in *Sand County* that isn't at least this complex in structure, but this complexity is transparent; the writing flows so beautifully the reader is unaware of being carried so far into the intricacies of ecology. This is where the power of *Sand County* lies. It also lies in the fact that the reader develops a firm trust in Leopold's words because these words are so clear and direct and because they are so obviously based on years of observation and thought. Leopold writes of what he knows. He knows Silphium has a long tap root because he himself dug and dug trying to get to the end of it; he knows the Silphium root sprouts easily because he saw it happen. One day he has seen a power shovel cut the root and asked himself: What will happen to this root? He then took the time to discover the answer. That he went back later to see what had occurred indicates not only his keen powers of observation, but also how he brought his intelligence and experience to bear on his observations. How could a reader fail to trust such a careful observer and chronicler of nature?

Other Riches

There is so much good stuff in *Sand County* that I could go on and on, about what Leopold has to say on mice and squirrels and oak trees (p. 27) or about species diversity on campus (p. 47). His "Odyssey" is one of his most fanciful pieces and is reminiscent of Primo Levi's (1984) story, "Carbon." In both, an atom is followed as it moves from the substance of one living thing to another in a fictional treatment of cycling. And I can't leave *Sand County* without mentioning Leopold's wry humor and down-to-earth approach as in:

There are two spiritual dangers in not owning a farm. One is the danger of supposing that breakfast comes from the grocery, and the other that heat comes from the furnace (p. 6).

To build a road is so much simpler than to think of what the country really needs (p. 101).

Open the crop of a fat little Mearns' quail and you find an herbarium of subsurface foods scratched from the rocky ground you thought barren (p. 151).

Now that I've come to appreciate *Sand County* so much more, I've asked myself why the book is so meaningful and why it has been so influential. One reason, as I mentioned, is the beautiful, yet very down-to-earth language Leopold uses. Another is the way he interweaves vivid descriptions with the deep insights in ecology. He presents the best ecological thinking of his day and thus produces a form of nature writing more substantive than most. It is also nature writing that deals more explicitly with the ethical and the aesthetic than is usually the case. For Leopold, beauty in nature was a reminder of obligation (Paul 1992). It may be that Leopold's writing was ahead of its time and that's why it did not become popular and well-known until the 1970s when the environmental movement increased people's awareness of the issues Leopold dealt with. The *Sand County* became "the bible" of the modern conservation/environmental movement" (Flader & Callicott 1991, p. 30), and Leopold became "the commonly acknowledged patron saint of American environmentalism" (Guha 1996, p. 210). The present interest in Leopold indicates that *Sand County* remains an important document among environmentalists (Buell 1995). But I think too much emphasis on its serious significance may blind people to the joyousness of Leopold's prose, and that's unfortunate. Yes, by all means, read *Sand County* for the messages contained there, but also savor not only what he says but how beautifully he says it. Though I hate to leave *Sand County*, I have to because there is so much more I want to say about Leopold. My only advice is to read or reread this book whenever you get the chance. Even if you are very familiar with it, I guarantee that you will find something new and fascinating in it, which is, I suppose, the sign that this book is truly a work of art.

Other Writings

While *Sand County* is the one book on which Leopold's reputation as a writer rests, he was a much more prolific writer than this slim volume would indicate. His textbook, *Game Management* (1933), is considered a classic in the field and is still in use. Early in his career with the U.S. Forest Service he began a newsletter called *The Pine Cone* for his fellow rangers, and as he became more involved in game management and conservation issues he wrote for a number of publications, both those for other professionals and for the general public. David E. Brown and Neil B. Carmony (1995) have edited a selection of these articles, ones dealing with the

Southwest. These include some early pieces from *The Pine Cone* as well as articles from a variety of publications, including some later book reviews that were written long after Leopold had moved to Wisconsin. What makes this volume particularly interesting is that Brown and Carmony have written a commentary following each article. In a number of cases they revisited the areas Leopold wrote about, and they report on what has happened to these forests and rivers and lakes since his time.

Susan L. Flader and J. Baird Callicott (1991), both noted Leopold scholars, have also edited a collection of his articles. Their volume is wider ranging, including entries from his boyhood journals, speeches, and articles, some of which were never published. "What Is a Weed?" is in the latter category that is one of my favorites because Leopold wryly sticks up for weeds as sources of biodiversity. Reading this book, it is interesting to see how his writing style varies with the purpose of the piece and how his ideas evolved over time. One thing that Flader and Callicott note is that Leopold had great skill in "reading both the landscape and historical descriptions of it in order to discover processes of environmental change" (p. 173), and that one of his primary objects in teaching wildlife ecology was to have students learn how to read the land.

A good example of his skill in reading the land is found in "Conservation," an essay in *Round River* (1953), a collection of unpublished essays and travel logs that Leopold's son, Luna, put together. In "Conservation," Aldo Leopold describes how long-term the effects of scarring the land can be. He writes of a mountain in Germany where one slope is covered with a rich oak forest and the opposite slope with a much less luxuriant pine forest:

> *Why? Because in the Middle Ages the south slope was preserved as a deer forest by a hunting bishop; the north slope was pastured, plowed, and cut by settlers, just as we do with our woodlots in Wisconsin and Iowa today. ... During this period of abuse something happened to the microscopic flora and fauna of the soil, [and] two centuries of conservation have not sufficed to restore these losses* (p. 147).

Here Leopold manages to make two points; to explain why scars on the land are so long-lasting and to remind the reader that scarring is a problem which also occurs much closer to home than Germany. This is only one of a number of good essays in *Round River*. "Blue River" is a short, but beautiful piece on a dead cow, and "Natural History: The Forgotten Science" is a great way to introduce students to how meaningful spending time with nature can be.

Critical Attention

   Round River and the other collections show that Leopold was a masterful writer, that *Sand County* was hardly a fluke. But it is only recently that his writing has been given any critical consideration. One spur for this study was the celebration in 1987 of the 100th anniversary of his birth on January 11, 1887. J. Baird Callicott (1987) edited a volume called *A Companion to* A Sand County Almanac: *Interpretive and Critical Essays;* it is a great resource because *Sand County* is looked at from such a variety of perspectives. There are two essays here by Curt Meine, who has written the most extensive biography of Leopold (1988); one deals with Leopold's early years and the other with how "The Land Ethic," the last essay in *Sand County,* was constructed from a number of earlier pieces and then rewritten several times. Susan Flader, who wrote the first book-length study on Leopold (*Thinking Like a Mountain,* 1974), writes of the sand county, really Sauk County, where Leopold had his shack. She goes into some detail on how the land was scarred and what has happened to it in the years since Leopold's death. There are also a number of essays on *Sand County* as a work of literature and as a work of ethics. Several commentators make the point that the book deals with three aspects of the land — its ecology, its aesthetics, and the ethical issues involved in its use — and with the relationship between these aspects that Leopold sees as very closely interconnected.

   Another volume (Tanner 1987) published at about the same time contains a few of the same essays as in the Callicott volume, but it also has some more personal pieces, including reminiscences by four of Leopold's children and an essay by his younger brother, Frederic. I found it interesting that Frederic, who spent his whole life in the Leopold family home in Burlington, Iowa, was, like his brother, an enthusiastic observer of nature. He became fascinated with wood ducks and studied their habits for over 40 years. He built nesting boxes in his yard and became the world authority on the nesting habits of this species. It is also worth noting that three of Leopold's five children — Starker, Luna and Estella — were members of the prestigious National Academy of Sciences, a unique achievement. This and other interesting pieces of information can be found in Marybeth Lorbiecki's (1996) biography of Leopold. It is much shorter and less detailed than Meine's and that is one of its strengths. Lorbiecki's book is more accessible and enjoyable, and I recommend it to those who want to learn more about Leopold but are not interested in the minutiae of his life. Another nice feature of this book is the large number of photographs it contains; they really bring Leopold to life. In a couple of the pictures he is smoking a cigarette, which may help to explain why a 61-year-old man who was thin, muscular, and very physically active died suddenly of a heart attack.

Besides the books I've mentioned that deal exclusively with Leopold, a number of other works consider his writing along with those of other nature writers. The interesting thing about these commentaries is that each author treats Leopold's work very differently, an indication of the richness to be found there. Sherman Paul (1992) focuses on Leopold's use of language, while James I. McClintock (1994) looks at the ethical and moral issues raised, and Frank Stewart (1995) at the aesthetic. In *The Idea of Wilderness*, Max Oelschlaeger (1991) examines the complexity of Leopold's views. He suggests that *Sand County* can be seen as having two poles or aspects: a negative and critical one, which prepares the way for the land ethic Leopold sketches at the end of the book, and a positive and affirmative pole which includes the statement of the land ethic itself with its implication that through right thinking and acting humans can husband the natural world.

Leopold and Ecology

Oelschlaeger also draws on the work of Donald Worster (1977) who classifies environmentalists into two categories: the arcadians who want to preserve nature and be one with it, and the imperialists who want to dominate and manage wild nature. Leopold does not fit comfortably into either category. In working for the U.S. Forest Service he was definitely in the imperial camp, but as his understanding of ecology deepened he became more arcadian, though he never gave up the idea that some management of nature was necessary. While Leopold was trained as a forester, he became more interested in the animal side of nature as his career progressed. This grew out of his personal interest in hunting and his growing sense that focusing on only one part of a natural environment was useless. He also became more and more interested in ecological thinking, especially after meeting the great British ecologist, Charles Elton, at an international conference on wildlife population cycles in Matamek, Quebec in 1931. Elton and Leopold began a correspondence that lasted until Leopold's death, and Elton and his family stayed with the Leopolds in Madison when Elton was lecturing at the University of Wisconsin. There is evidence that these two great names in ecology from either side of the Atlantic were influences on each other. A lot of Leopold's thinking, including his interest in food webs and invasions of non-native species, obviously grew out of Elton's work.

But it would be a mistake to see all of Leopold's thinking as derivative. One of his most novel ideas is that of the health of the land. He defined health as the capacity of internal self-renewal and noted that "there are two organisms whose processes of self-renewal have been subjected to human interference and control. One of these is man himself (medicine and public health). The other is land (agriculture and conservation). The effort to control the health of land has not been very successful" (Leopold 1949, p. 194). What comes through here is that Leopold sees the land as an organism. This grows out of his interest in the work of the Russian philosopher P.D. Ouspensky, who saw all parts of the environment as alive and as working together as a whole. Leopold argues that "a science of land health needs, first of all, a base datum of normality, a picture of how healthy land maintains itself as an organism" (Leopold 1949, p. 196). This is why wilderness is so important; it can serve as a laboratory for the study of land health. Humans have been so inept in maintaining the health of lands which they have altered that only wilderness can provide a guide to restoring the land's health. Perhaps this is a good note on which to end this essay, a good thought to carry away from Leopold's work. The efforts to preserve and improve land health have increased since Leopold's day, but the forces acting to destroy the land have also increased in efficiency. Leopold had no panaceas for his time or ours, but his beautiful language and beautiful ideas will continue to foster environmentalism well into the next century.

Note: I am grateful for the opportunity I had to do research for this article during the 1997 National Endowment for the Humanities Summer Institute "The Environmental Imagination" at Vassar College.

References

Brown, D.E. & Carmony, N.B. (Eds.). (1995). *Aldo Leopold's Southwest.* Albuquerque, NM: University of New Mexico Press.

Buell, L. (1995). *The Environmental Imagination: Thoreau, Nature Writing, and the Formation of American Culture.* Cambridge, MA: Harvard University Press.

Callicott, J.B. (Ed.). (1987). *Companion to* A Sand County Almanac: *Interpretive and Critical Essays.* Madison, WI: University of Wisconsin Press.

Flader, S.L. (1974). *Thinking Like a Mountain: Aldo Leopold and the Evolution of an Ecological Attitude Toward Deer, Wolves, and Forests.* Columbia, MO: University of Missouri Press.

Flader, S.L. & Callicott, J.B. (Eds.). (1991). *The River of the Mother of God and Other Essays by Aldo Leopold.* Madison, WI: University of Wisconsin Press.

Fritzell, P. (1990). *Nature Writing and America.* Ames, IA: Iowa State Press.

Guha, R. (1996). Lewis Mumford, the forgotten American environmentalist: An essay in rehabilitation. In D. Macauley (Ed.), *Minding Nature: The Philosophers of Ecology* (pp. 209-228). New York: Guilford.

Leopold, A. (1933). *Game Management.* New York: Scribner's.

Leopold, A. (1949). *A Sand County Almanac.* New York: Oxford University Press.

Leopold, L. (Ed.). (1953). *Round River: From the Journal of Aldo Leopold.* New York: Oxford University Press.

Levi, P. (1984). *The Periodic Table* (R. Rosenthal, Trans.). New York: Schocken.

Lorbiecki, M. (1996). *Aldo Leopold: A Fierce Green Fire.* Helena, MT: Falcon.

McClintock, J.I. (1994). *Nature's Kindred Spirits.* Madison, WI: University of Wisconsin Press.

Meine, C. (1988). *Aldo Leopold: His Life and Work.* Madison, WI: University of Wisconsin Press.

Oelschlaeger, M. (1991). *The Idea of Wilderness.* New Haven, CT: Yale University Press.

Paul, S. (1992). *For Love of the World: Essays on Nature Writers.* Iowa City, IA: University of Iowa Press.

Stewart, F. (1995). *The Natural History of Nature Writing.* Washington, DC: Island Press.

Tanner, T. (Ed.). (1987). *Aldo Leopold: The Man and his Legacy.* Ankeny, IA: Soil Conservation Society of America.

Vukelich, G. (1987). *North County Notebook.* Madison, WI: North Country Press.

Worster, D. (1977). *Nature's Economy: The Roots of Ecology.* San Francisco: Sierra Club.

Looking into Dioramas

At the Bell Museum of Natural History in Minneapolis, there are rooms filled with dioramas portraying the animals and ecosystems of the upper Midwest. At the end of one row of dioramas is a particularly elaborate one depicting a beaver dam with one beaver slapping mud onto the structure, another gnawing at a tree, and still others on the riverbank. When you turn the corner heading for the next series of displays, you realize that there's a small side window to this diorama, and when you look in, you see the snug interior of the dam, complete with a female beaver and her offspring. There is even a platform outside this window so young visitors can step up to get a good look at the scene.

I come from New York City, the home of the American Museum of Natural History (AMNH), so I've been familiar with dioramas my whole life. Maybe familiarity does breed contempt, because I've rarely given this museum display form much thought, considering it rather dated and not as exciting as some of the newer, more interactive exhibits. Yet when I visit the museum, I probably linger longer at the dioramas than at any other exhibit. There is something mesmerizing about these scenes; my eye is drawn into them, and the longer I look, the more I see. I haven't done a scientific study on this, but I know my stepsons loved the dioramas, too — almost as much as the dinosaurs — and even my husband couldn't tear himself away from some of them. But my favorite diorama is not at the AMNH, it is at the University of Minnesota in Bell Museum: it's the beavers. The little window giving a behind-the-scenes view makes all the difference. There are other great exhibits at the Bell, including a platform covered with a waterbed-like carpet that is meant to resemble sphagnum moss; you are invited to walk across it to get a feeling for what it would be like to slog through a bog in the boundary waters of northern Minnesota. There is also a children's room filled with specimens to be touched. I didn't have a child with me, but my visit was still memorable — where else would I get a chance to examine an elephant skull or to pat a buffalo on its head and feel its thick, wiry hair? But I'm getting off the track. It is dioramas I want to write about here.

The Roots of Dioramas

Since visiting the Bell Museum, I've done a little research on the history of dioramas. While they evolved into their most developed form during the first third of the 20th century, their roots can be traced back into the early 19th century to the Philadelphia natural history museum of the artist, naturalist, and museum entrepreneur, Charles Willson Peale. He was one of the first to use fossil bones to construct the skeleton of an extinct animal; in this case, the impressive skeleton of a mastodon that he and his family had excavated at a farm in upstate New York. Peale's museum also contained a large number of stuffed animals, especially birds. He and his children were taxidermy artists who created specimens with very life-like poses and often set them against painted backgrounds depicting the birds' natural habitats.

The Peale museum was closed because of financial problems by the 1840s, but another form of public display was developing that was important to the history of dioramas, and this is the panorama. In the era before motion pictures and television, many forms of visual display were popular. The people of the 19th century seemed to crave such displays, the more spectacular the better. The panorama was a type of visual entertainment particularly popular in the United States. Huge canvases were painted with dramatic or historically significant scenes, and admission was charged to view them. One of these panoramas has been reconstructed at the Metropolitan Museum of Art in New York. It covers the walls of a circular room and depicts the Palace of Versailles and its garden.

Another influence on the development of dioramas was the interest in using natural objects in interior decorating. In the second half of the 19th century, not only were Wardian cases that enclosed groupings of plants, snails and other small animals popular, but so were aquariums (Gould 1997). Stuffed animals were considered attractive accent pieces for a room, with a deer's head a sign of hunting prowess and a beautifully plumed bird a symbol of aesthetic sensibility. As the century progressed, there were more displays of stuffed animals outside the home. Taxidermy had become an art, with the animals set in life-like and dramatic poses. It was popular to exhibit animals in theatrical groupings at exhibitions and fairs. The famous centennial exhibition in Philadelphia in 1876 saw the height of the fame of Martha Maxwell, an accomplished hunter and taxidermist from Colorado who created a large display of animals of the West set against a background of trees and bushes (Benson 1986).

Karen Wonders (1989) sees a connection between the elaborate animal sculptures of such artists as Antoine-Louis Barye and dramatic groupings of stuffed animals such as a scene by the French naturalist and taxidermist Jules Verreaux showing an Arab on a camel being attacked by two lions. Barye also portrayed animals in dramatic poses, sometimes in combat; his bronzes were the most highly valued sculptures of the group of "animaliers" who worked in France during the mid-to-late 19th century. While Barye never visited Africa or Asia, he spent a great deal of time at Paris' Jardin des Plantes where there was both a zoo and a natural history museum (Baillio 1994). He was a careful student of animal anatomy and received permission to dissect and sketch the remains of animals after they had died at the zoo. The works of Barye and Verreaux indicate the 19th-century public's interest in realistic scenes portraying large animals in dramatic poses.

Early Dioramas

The sensational displays of the lions-fighting-camel genre gave way to groupings of animals in more realistic poses and composed of species that were more likely to be found in close proximity to each other. These displays were usually encased in glass for protection. Often, the base of the display was molded to look like the terrain in the animals' habitat. From this type of display, it was a rather small step to place a grouping in a niche set in a wall, paint the niche's walls to look like sky and distant hills or plains, and add native plants to the material at the base. The noted Swedish artist Bruno Liljefors was responsible for the background paintings in some of the best early dioramas which were constructed in Sweden in the 1890s (Fredlund 1988). But even the first crude attempts at such displays were so well received by the public that museum personnel were encouraged to greater heights of verisimilitude. Over time, the displays became larger and more elaborate with more realistically painted backdrops and greater numbers of animals set into more complex grounds that attempted to reproduce the topography of an area and the types of plants found there. In this way the diorama was born – or the habitat group, as it was christened by Frank Chapman. He was a master of the art and an expert on birds who spent most of his career at the AMNH, where you can still see many examples of his work.

Creating dioramas became a complex art, an art based on scientific knowledge of the plants, animals and habitats displayed – but an art nonetheless – and one that became more and more refined as time went on. In the early dioramas, the animals were often shown in dramatic poses and were set very obviously against the backgrounds, while in the wild they would be much more likely to be hiding from predators. Gregg Mitman (1993) writes of a display of Komodo dragons at the AMNH in which one of these animals is shown with a wild boar in its mouth and another in a raised-head posture reminiscent of the way dinosaurs are often portrayed. These are two postures that were documented in a film made of Komodo dragons in their natural surroundings, but these are rare postures chosen to be used in the diorama because they were the two most dramatic behaviors seen. So even when dioramas were becoming more realistic, their creators had a hard time giving up the impulse to design crowd pleasers.

As time went on, greater pains were also taken with the design of the floor of the diorama and the backdrop. For those familiar with dioramas, it may seem surprising that the only things "real" in them are often the animals, but this is in fact the case since few of the plants are real. Though the early habitat groups included dried specimens, they didn't look very realistic or appealing and they weren't very durable, so they were soon replaced by leaves, flowers, etc. made of paper, silk, wax – any durable material the artists could find that would produce a realistic effect. In the gorilla habitat group at the AMNH, there are 75,000 artificial leaves and flowers, including a blackberry bush that took eight months to create (Hellman 1969). The rocks, ground, water and many other elements of the terrain were also made of artificial materials – the art of illusion was highly developed here. If a particular large tree caught the eye of the diorama designer, a plaster cast was taken of it, so that it could be reproduced exactly. The background painters also aimed for realism, something that made their work long underappreciated because they were working at the time when abstract art was coming to the fore.

Francis Lee Jaques

Recently I've become interested in the art of Francis Lee Jaques, one of the most accomplished of the diorama artists who worked for the AMNH. From an early age, he was interested in drawing and in wildlife, but for years he had to earn a living at jobs such as railroad fireman. Jacques' father wrote articles for *Field and Stream,* and through this connection Francis began doing illustrations for the magazine. After serving in the army during World War I, he worked as a commercial artist. In 1924, he sent three paintings of birds, his specialty, to Frank Chapman at the AMNH. Chapman was so impressed with Jaques' work, especially with the fact that Jaques had correctly painted the reversed wing coverts of the black duck, that he offered the artist a job at the museum (Luce & Andrews 1982). Jaques' first project there was to paint the domed ceiling of the Hall of Oceanic Birds, and this spectacular work can still be seen at the Museum. It shows a beautiful sky with soft clouds and birds of several species flying across it; there are also birds suspended from the ceiling and in some cases Jaques' painted birds are so life-like that it's difficult to tell them from the real birds.

Jaques remained at the Museum for 18 years doing dozens of diorama backgrounds, including all 18 in the Hall of Oceanic Birds. He traveled widely studying the areas he would reproduce in dioramas. He worked hard on developing tricks to get the viewer's eye to accept the flat background of the diorama as an expansive space that stretched to the horizon. He painted animals and plants on glass plates to give an illusion of depth, and in a rain forest diorama, he used mirrors to give an illusion of height (Hammond 1986). While some diorama painters were more realistic in their approach, his style resulted in particularly riveting scenes.

Jaques was an accomplished artist in other media as well. He produced beautiful oil paintings and watercolors, and also illustrated more than 50 books. These include three by the nature writer Sigurd Olson (1956, 1961a, 1961b) and two by the Justice of the Supreme Court, William O. Douglas (1960, 1961), who was a lifelong champion of conservation and who wrote extensively on his wilderness experiences. Jaques also illustrated several books written by his wife, Florence Jaques, describing their travels. I've just read *As Far as the Yukon* (1951), the lightly told story of their trip to the Northwest. The black-and-white illustrations by Jaques that fill the book are of a quality well above those usually found accompanying text, and they are a beautiful complement to Florence Jaques' writing. Jaques left the AMNH in 1942 so he could devote more time to book illustration. He also did freelance work on dioramas at a number of museums, including the Bell Museum in Minneapolis, though he was not responsible for the background for the beaver diorama. By the time he died in 1969, Jaques had created an impressive body of work which lives on in the books he illustrated and the dioramas he helped to create, most of which are still intact.

Creating an Illusion

Art is at the heart of the diorama experience. While natural history museum curators, usually scientists, were involved in decisions about what the diorama subjects would be and what animals and plants they would contain, the selection of the exact location to be reproduced and the layout of the diorama was often the province of artists. While the habitats reproduced in the dioramas were absolutely faithful to nature, the precise viewpoint used and the arrangement presented were often left to artists who created scenes that were pleasing to the eye, revealed as much information as possible about the habitat, and gave the illusion of reality. Taxidermy itself is an art, especially as it was practiced in natural history museums. For larger animals, the skeleton was constructed in a natural pose, then muscles of clay were molded on the skeleton, and such features as prominent blood vessels were added. A plaster cast of the model was made, and the animal's skin was fitted over it. Glass eyes and other features were then added, including such fine points as hints of saliva around the animal's mouth (Preston 1986).

Using materials that are not very natural at all — paper leaves, plastic water, plaster rocks — in the space of a small room, artists created the illusion of a wilderness scene, a scene into which humans do not seem to have ever intruded. In most dioramas, there is no hint of human activity, except in those that focus on humans, usually in halls of anthropology. The dioramas were designed to create a direct experience between the visitor and the natural world, and this experience was based primarily on the illusion that the visitor is looking through a window at an expanse of land filled with life rather than a tiny room filled with dead animals and artificial scenery (Wonders 1990). The illusion of reality was important to the purposes of the habitat group as they were envisioned by museum officials. While natural history museums had been set up as research establishments to further knowledge of the natural world, they were also intended to educate the public about the world. It was toward the end of the 19th century that the museums began to take this second part of their mission more seriously. Coincidentally, this was also the era of many social reform movements that saw education as essential to improving the lot of the lower classes.

The Purposes of Dioramas

Henry Fairfield Osborn, who headed the AMNH in the early years of this century, saw dioramas as providing the city-bound with experiences of the natural world. A visit to the museum with time spent looking at dioramas was like a day in the wilderness; it gave people a feeling for nature, for being one with the natural world. This may seem far-fetched to us today, but it was an important reason why the dioramas had to be so realistic: they were seen as replacements for the real thing. The second aim of the habitat groups was to give people an appreciation for the wonders of the natural world so they would be more willing to support projects to preserve the environment. Destruction of wilderness areas in the United States had become so severe by the end of the 19th century that a number of conservation efforts blossomed at this time.

Osborn and other museum leaders saw the conservation movement as an important source of support for museum activities (Rainger 1991). As a member of New York's wealthy elite himself, Osborn was in a position to encourage members of this elite who were interested in conservation to support museum activities as one of the most effective ways to educate the public about the seriousness of the problem and what was at stake. He argued that city dwellers had little understanding of the richness of life on Earth and the wonders of wilderness, and giving them a taste for these would add to the political backing for further conservation efforts. A great deal of the money Osborn collected was used to fund voyages throughout the world. This was the age of museum expeditions by people like Roy Chapman Andrews, who explored Central Asia and brought back huge numbers of animal skins and fossils as well as a great deal of information about the ecology of the Gobi Desert and other areas in Mongolia. Other groups went to Africa and South America on similar expeditions, so a massive number of specimens and a great deal of information were pouring into the AMNH. Most of the information ended up in research reports because, after all, the museum had been founded as a research institution as well as for education. Osborn's clever fund-raising strategies provided support for a great deal of research, often clothed as necessary preparations for new exhibits.

Other Display Forms

In her history of dioramas, Karen Wonders (1989, 1990) argues that habitat groups only became popular museum display forms in the United States and in Sweden where there was an interest in ecology as well as a tendency to romanticize the wilderness. While I haven't done extensive research on this, it is true that the Natural History Museum of London, the Museum of Comparative Zoology in Cambridge, and the Musée Histoire Naturelle in Paris are all set up very differently from such United States institutions as the AMNH. While there are many fossils, skeletons and stuffed animals displayed in the European museums, there are almost no habitat groups. Wonders sees this as a result of a different museum philosophy; these museums were designed primarily as research institutions, with education of the public as only a secondary concern. Many of the older exhibits show a large number of species arrayed one after another, just the kind of thing a taxonomist can use to study species differences, though museum officials argue that it also sends a message to the visitor about the tremendous diversity of life on Earth.

When the Musée Histoire Naturelle in Paris was reopened a few years ago after extensive renovations, many of the stuffed animals that had been exhibited previously were put into storage. The number of specimens displayed was pared down to make room for more explanatory exhibits. The only place dioramas were created was in the lower floor dealing with marine life; here visitors are given the feeling, as they walk through the exhibit where the lighting is very dim, that they are floating through a watery environment with specimens overhead in glass-enclosed dioramas. On the floor above, the focal exhibit of the museum is a great atrium which can be seen from all the upper floors as a parade of stuffed animals beginning with a giraffe and an elephant. This display has a Noah's ark-like look to it and is far from a habitat group.

Criticisms of Dioramas

As the European museum curators' attitude toward dioramas suggests, there are problems with this display form. Franz Boas criticized life groups, the equivalent of habitat groups for the display of indigenous peoples in typical settings, as having a number of limitations that also apply to habitat groups (Jacknis 1985). No matter how realistic such scenes are, there is a limit to the realism since these groups are housed within a museum setting; the viewer looking away from a display is instantly reminded of the ruse. Also, impressive display techniques can distract viewers from learning from the exhibit. The viewer may, for example, be intrigued by the way the illusion of a pool of water has been created and not pay attention to the animals in the diorama. Another problem is the dulling of effect through repetition; the wonder the viewer experiences in looking at the first diorama usually wears off long before they get to the 20th.

Donna Haraway's (1989) criticism of the habitat groups at the AMNH is more ideological. She sees them as epitomes of male science. She argues that they were created by a largely male staff including taxidermists like Carl Akeley, an expert in the diorama form at the AMNH who saw hunting for specimens as an important part of the job. Akeley was responsible for planning the Hall of African Mammals, though he didn't live to see it completed. In melodramatic fashion, he died while on a safari hunting animals for the Hall's exhibits. Haraway notes that while the animal groupings in these dioramas might include males, females and young of the same species, the male specimen more often than not is given the most prominent position. When I visited the AMNH after reading this, I found it be very true: here was one of those things that only becomes obvious (at least to me) after it was pointed out. Haraway sees subtle cues like this giving the message to all viewers that the male is dominant in all species. She also sees the whole process of creating these dioramas as being a glorification of the male in science, with male curators, artists and staff, often accompanied by wealthy hunters, going off on expeditions around the world, overpowering and killing the animals they needed, and thus taking control of the natural world. These dioramas at least implicitly glorify hunting, the domination of nature, and the use of nature for human purposes.

The limitations of this display form have helped bring the great age of dioramas to a close. While some are still being constructed, it is unlikely that they will ever become as popular as they once were. Despite Osborn's argument that they provide rich experiences of nature, the focus today is on the fact that they are illusions which send the message that the natural world is something that we should separate ourselves from and that should be kept under glass. Today's environmentalists argue that such isolation of humans from the living world is the source of many of our problems: we do not understand this world because we have so little contact with it. While this viewpoint is valid, it seems a shame not to take full advantage of the dioramas that do exist. Though it's important to recognize their limitations, they do provide a glimpse at exciting aspects of nature. They allow us to get some sense of environments we are unlikely to visit, they are beautiful examples of art and science working together, *and* they are fun to look at. Where else, I may ask, is someone like me going to see the inside of a beaver's dam?

References

Baillio, J. (1994). *The Wild Kingdom of Antoine-Louis Barye.* New York: Wildenstein.

Benson, M. (1986). *Martha Maxwell: Rocky Mountain Naturalist.* Lincoln, NE: University of Nebraska Press.

Douglas, W.O. (1960). *My Wilderness – The Pacific West.* New York: Doubleday.

Douglas, W.O. (1960). *My Wilderness – East to Katahdin.* New York: Doubleday.

Fredlund, B. (Ed.). (1988). *In the Realm of the Wild: The Art of Bruno Liljefors of Sweden.* Gothenburg, Sweden: Göteborgs Konstmuseum.

Gould, S.J. (1997). Seeing eye to eye. *Natural History, 106*(7), 14-18, 60-62.

Hammond, N. (1986). *Twentieth-Century Wildlife Artists.* Woodstock, NY: Overlook.

Haraway, D. (1989). *Primate Visions: Gender, Race, and Nature in the World of Modern Science.* New York: Routledge.

Hellman, G. (1969). *Bankers, Bones and Beetle: The First Century of The American Museum of Natural History.* Garden City, NY: Natural History Press.

Jacknis, I. (1985). Franz Boas and exhibits: On the limitations of the museum method of anthropology. In G.W. Stocking, Jr. (Ed.), *Objects and Others: Essays on Museums and Material Culture* (pp. 75-111). Madison, WI: University of Wisconsin Press.

Jaques, F.P. (1951). *As Far as the Yukon.* New York: Harper's.

Luce, D. & Andrews, L. (1982). *Francis Lee Jaques: Artist-Naturalist.* Minneapolis, MN: University of Minnesota Press.

Mitman, G. (1993). Cinematic nature: Hollywood technology, popular culture, and The American Museum of Natural History. *Isis, 84,* 637-661.

Olson, S. (1956). *The Singing Wilderness.* New York: Knopf.

Olson, S. (1961a). *Listening Point.* New York: Knopf.

Olson, S. (1961b). *The Lonely Land.* New York: Knopf.

Preston, D. (1986). *Dinosaurs in the Attic: An Excursion into The American Museum of Natural History.* New York: St. Martin's.

Rainger, R. (1991). *An Agenda for Antiquity: Henry Fairfield Osborn and Vertebrate Paleontology at The American Museum of Natural History, 1890-1935.* Tuscaloosa, AL: University of Alabama Press.

Wonders, K. (1989). Exhibiting fauna – From spectacle to habitat group. *Curator, 32*(2), 131-156.

Wonders, K. (1990). The illusionary art of background painting in habitat dioramas. *Curator, 33*(2), 90-118.

How To See It

Joseph Wood Krutch was a professor of literature and a theater critic, who after years of living in the East, discovered the Southwest and eventually moved there. In *The Desert Year* (1952) he enthusiastically describes why he finds the natural history of the Southwest so fascinating. Though he had long enjoyed observing nature near his country home in Connecticut, the organisms and environment in the Southwest were so different that he found himself looking at a totally new world as if with new and more observant eyes. In an essay titled "How To See It," he writes:

> *Perhaps I shall never again see any of these things quite as completely as I do now at this moment when I have grown just sufficiently accustomed to my new environment to be able to take it in but by no means accustomed enough to take it for granted* (p. 46).

The naturalist John Burroughs (1992), in an essay called "The Art of Seeing Things," takes an opposite tack: the better you know an area, the more you will see there. While Burroughs did do some traveling, many of his essays describe what he discovered about the natural world close to his rural home in New York State. For him, the better one knows an area and its plants and animals, the more likely the eye is to pick up interesting detail. In another essay, "A Sharp Outlook," Burroughs (1981) quotes Gilbert White, the author of *The Natural History of Selborne* and one of the founders of the nature writing tradition, as holding that "the locality would be found the richest in zoological or botanical specimens which was most thoroughly examined" (p. 22).

Burroughs and Krutch seem to be at odds about the conditions under which one is likely to be most observant. Krutch thinks that the eye gets sated, dulled, by looking at the same thing again and again; one sees less because the eye takes things for granted. Burroughs, on the other hand, thinks that with knowledge of an area, it's easier for the eye to look beyond the basics for the minute details. But notwithstanding these differences, I think Burroughs and Krutch would agree that what is most obvious to the eye is the unusual, that which sticks out against the background of the usual; the difference is in how they define the unusual. Krutch sees it in a totally different environment, where everything is unusual relative to the environment from which he came. For Burroughs, however, the unusual means something more subtle, the small variations that occur from day to day, and that only someone very familiar with an area would notice.

It is interesting that despite their differences, both Burroughs and Krutch wrote essays on seeing. And they are hardly the only nature writers to do so. In her *Pilgrim at Tinker Creek*, Annie Dillard (1974) has an essay called "Seeing" in which she writes of looking at everything from microorganisms to meteor showers. In *Round River* (1953), Aldo Leopold describes the responses of four of his friends when he pointed out a new deer swath to them. He notes that:

> There are four categories of outdoors men: deer hunters, duck hunters, bird hunters, and non-hunters. These categories have nothing to do with sex or age, or accouterments; they represent four diverse habits of the human eye. The deer hunter habitually watches the next bend; the duck hunter watches the skyline; the bird hunter watches the dog; the non-hunter does not watch (p. 126).

This passage stuck with me because it reminds me of something I read a long time ago, something written by Rudolf Arnheim (1974), who is interested in the psychology of art. He argues that seeing is much more than a passive intake of images by the brain, that it involves great mental activity and is dependent upon prior experience, what the mind has already learned. This is really what Leopold, Dillard, Burroughs and Krutch are all writing about: how our interests and our knowledge influence what we see. It makes sense that naturalists would write about seeing because it is so central to most experiences of nature. Yet seeing seems such a simple thing, so easy to do, that we tend to take it for granted. Even though biology is a science in which observation has always played a pivotal role, we tend to see observation as something anyone can do, a lower-order thinking skill that even a first-grader can master. While this may be the case, seeing does deserve more attention; we should not discount a skill just because it can be learned by a small child. Douglas Burton-Christie (1996) describes how his three-year-old daughter has taught him to see; she was so observant that he found himself noticing a lot more. He quotes Krutch to the effect that seeing is the faculty of wonder that requires time, patience and attention; we get better at seeing the more we attend to it.

The Intelligent Eye

This brings me to David Perkins' *The Intelligent Eye* (1994). As I noted then, Perkins argues that by learning to look at art and think about it, we can develop thinking skills useful in many disciplines. Having tried his approach, I have to agree with him, and I think his method can just as well be used for looking at cells or the internal anatomy of a frog. Perkins gives a four-step method of how to look at a work of art. The first step is to give time to looking, 10 minutes or so. Ten minutes is a long time to stare at a picture, and I'll admit that I rarely do it. But even a couple of minutes is longer than we ordinarily attend to any image, and such attention bears rich fruit. The longer we look at an image or at a living organism, the more we see; small details or slight differences in shading that at first weren't noticeable become quite obvious, and the mind begins to work, asking questions about why the artist chose to include this and exclude that. As Perkins notes, "if giving looking time is important for art, giving thinking time is important in general" (p. 42). I find that in our culture taking time to think is not encouraged. We are doers, not thinkers. Taking time to sit and quietly ponder a problem — or simply to look and think about what we are seeing — is not something we allow ourselves to do often enough, but as Perkins points out, it is useful, no matter what discipline is involved.

After taking time to look, we can move on to Perkins' second step: making looking broad and adventurous. Here, too, the starting point is looking, but the tie to thinking is closer, and the viewer is encouraged to expand perceptions by looking and asking questions of the painting that force the mind to think more daringly about the image. Perkins suggests looking for symbolism, surprises, cultural and historical connections, virtuosity, etc. In other words, he wants the viewer to think of the image in many different ways, on many different levels. This exercise could easily be done with a photograph of a cell or by looking at a cell through a microscope and asking: what kind of cell is this; is it a unicellular organism or a cell from a larger organism; what makes it distinctive; how does it differ from a textbook illustration of a cell; what seems to have been done to the cell to make it visible, etc. No matter what the subject, the aim here is to ask a lot of different questions, to look at the image from many different viewpoints, even viewpoints that may, at first, seem odd; we are not to censure our minds but to let them be adventurous because it's hard to predict where a fruitful idea will come from.

After this broad-ranging approach, Perkins suggests switching gears a bit for step three: making looking clear and deep. He notes that:

> *If you give looking time and look broadly and adventurously, you will certainly discover much. ... But it is all too easy not to. Time and broad thinking can still just skim the surface. ... We reach easy conclusions that may not stand up to more careful scrutiny* (p. 59).

The antidote to this is thinking more deeply; questioning the observations we've made, following them further to see if they hold up and are perhaps even more fruitful if they are given more careful consideration. Again, such sober deliberation is something that our culture doesn't encourage; we are too impatient, too anxious to get on with it, to produce results. Yet any endeavor, whether it be art or biology or economics, benefits from careful thought. Problem solving has been a buzzword in education for years and learning problem solving skills can be very useful for students. But Perkins is arguing that there are other ways to encourage thinking, and analyzing an image is one of them. While he focuses on artworks, I think looking clear and deep, going back to what we've already considered and questioning conclusions, is a valuable technique to use with any image.

The fourth step in Perkins' scheme is a summing-up step, a tying together of loose ends, by reviewing the three steps already taken. Again, this is something we tend to neglect in our efforts to be done with a task, but it is good to take stock, to review what we've accomplished in our looking. Perkins suggests that it is useful to organize the process of looking — to do it in some order, such as the one he recommends — so that the process is systematic and nothing is slipped over. He also suggests that the process outlined here can, with variations, be used in a variety of different contexts aside from the examination of artworks. As I mentioned, I find it works well with specimens, biological illustrations, and photographs of specimens. Asking these questions forces the observer to think beyond simply identifying the specimen or figuring out the diagram and to ask questions such as: Why is this illustration colored the way it is? Why did the photographer choose this angle for the photo? What assumptions underlie this representation of the living world? Since biology is such a visual science it behooves us to look more closely at the images we use in teaching and also at how we help our students to view the living world.

Thinking about Perkins' recommendations reminded me of an old book that is one of my favorites, May Theilgaard Watts' (1975) *Reading the Landscape of America*. Watts was a botanist who traveled widely in the United States and describes the various areas she visited, not only in terms of what they look like now, but how they got to be that way. She reads the landscape, very much as Perkins reads a picture, bringing to bear a wealth of knowledge and perceptual skill that allow her to understand what she sees much better than most people would. The shape of a sand dune in Indiana along the shore of Lake Michigan tells her a great deal about how they developed over time and about the different plants that have been involved in this development. In another chapter, she "reads" the record of a quaking bog as it evolved from a lake that slowly filled in. Though some of her material is dated, almost any of Watts' chapters is a wonderful way to introduce the concept of change over time in an ecosystem and also a great example of what thoughtful seeing is all about.

Seeing and Art

Someone who reads seemingly more mundane landscapes than Watts is Mary Ann McLean, who has created a book filled with drawings of the plants in her garden. This hardly sounds revolutionary, but what makes *Mary Anne's Garden* unique is that McLean (1987) draws the same plant day after day, or in some cases hour after hour, creating what amount to time-lapse sketches of flowers and vegetables. But she thinks calling them time-lapse drawings "sounds like a bit of a yawn," and instead she considers these drawings as "the surprises and excitements of things growing" (p. 8). What a beautiful way to put it; what a wonderful way to express the joy of seeing.

The joy of seeing – and of recording what's seen in art – are also the subjects of two other beautiful books: *Bird Egg Feather Nest* by Maryjo Koch (1992) and *A Trail Through Leaves: The Journal as a Path to Place* by Hannah Hinchman (1997). Koch's book includes striking watercolors of everything from birds' eggs to birds' feet. Unlike McLean, she has traveled far from her backyard and includes birds as diverse as owls, flamingos and penguins. What makes the book so striking is the interesting way text and drawings are combined and woven seamlessly together. Hannah Hinchman's book combines some of the aspects of McLean's and Koch's, but has a very different flavor. Hers is more a how-to book, in the best sense of the term. The book is the story of how she came to find it so rewarding to keep a visual journal of her observations on nature; interspersed throughout the book are sections on how the reader can also develop such a journal. This is both an inspiring book and a beautiful one. It is liberally illustrated with sketches from Hinchman's journals of everything from rocks and deer to lichen and beetles. While I enjoyed McLean's and Koch's books, it was only when I read Hinchman that I became interested in drawing from nature. She made me want to force myself to see more carefully, to really savor what I was looking at, and drawing is the best way to do this.

Drawing To See

I know that on more than one occasion in these columns, I've used the quote from Goethe to the effect that you really haven't looked at an object until you have drawn it, but I think this bears repeating here. I discovered this anew when I started to put Hinchman's ideas into practice. But even well before I read her book, I've tried to get my students to do some drawing. I reasoned that if I am going to help students to observe more carefully, then I should be putting more emphasis on drawing, something that is seen as appropriate for three-year-olds, but beneath the dignity of the "mature" high school or college student. When I ask my students to draw, often their first response is to look at me in disbelief. But then I sense a nervousness, a feeling that this is something they simply can't do. They can't do it because they don't see themselves as artists. Also, they are out of practice – it has been a long time since a teacher has asked them to draw. Lest you think that I'm asking them to reproduce Da Vinci's anatomical sketches or to draw a bird's-eye view of the campus, I should note that what I usually ask them to draw first is an unshelled peanut. But even this simple exercise does get Goethe's point across; they do "know" that peanut a lot better after they have completed their drawings.

Robert McKim (1980) argues that drawing invigorates seeing. In his book, *Experiences in Visual Thinking*, he describes how seeing, imagining and drawing are related to each other. He considers visual thinking a powerful mental ability that is usually not well developed because our educational system, after the primary grades, ignores visual education and concentrates instead on language and reasoning skills. McKim provides exercises designed to train the mind to imagine more effectively. Drawing is an important part of his program, as are exercises in how to observe more carefully and to imagine more richly.

Seeing and Microscopy

Because biologists do not just see with the naked eye, but with a variety of instruments – most notably the microscope – emphasis on the education of vision is especially important. I can remember the first time I wrestled with a microscope as a high school freshman. It was a frustrating rather than an exciting experience; I hardly felt the kind of breathless awe that van Leeuwenhoek describes (Ruestow 1996). I finally saw the cells in the onion root tip, but not before I had cracked a few cover slips and gotten completely frustrated. It would have helped if someone had pointed out to me that my problems were hardly unique, that they were in part the result of the fact that, as Ian Hacking (1981) puts it: the first lesson of microscopy is that we learn to see through a microscope by doing, not just by looking. We have to learn to move around in the microscopic world, and just as we often fall as we learn to walk around in the macroscopic world, it's not surprising that we might break a few cover slips in our wanderings in the microscopic world.

James Elkins (1996) writes that all seeing is difficult, that it is not just when using a microscope that we encounter problems:

> *No matter how hard I try, there will be things I do not see. No seeing sees everything, and no skill or practice can alter that. Every field of vision is clotted with sexuality, desire, convention, anxiety, and boredom, and nothing is available for full, leisurely inspection. Seeing is also inconstant seeing, partial seeing, poor seeing, and not seeing: seeing is also blindness* (p. 95).

This is a discouraging comment, but it highlights the point Arnheim makes: that seeing involves the mind as much as it involves the eye, and so the mind's prior knowledge – to say nothing of the emotions – influence what we see. In an article on early microscopy, Elkins (1992) gives an example of how mind and eye interact. He notes that it was difficult for people like van Leeuwenhoek to make sense of what they saw under the microscope because it was so totally foreign; the mind could not grasp what the eye saw because it had no context in which to put these images.

In a book on 17th-century Dutch art, Svetlana Alpers (1983) writes of the relationship between this art and the use of the microscope by such Dutchmen as van Leeuwenhoek and Christian Huygens. She is not arguing that the art of the time influenced the microscopy or vice versa, though there was definitely communication between artists and microscopists with, for example, van Leeuwenhoek serving as executor of Vermeer's estate. Instead, she sees both the art and the interest in microscopy as stemming from the same cultural source: a basic interest in what things look like. This was a culture in which images played a prominent role. Constantijn Huygens, the father of Christian, wrote that the eye is the source of new knowledge about the world, that we learn by seeing. He and other Dutch thinkers of the time were influenced by the writings of Francis Bacon, or at least by those portions of Bacon's writings in which he argues for the importance of careful observation: "All depends on keeping the eye steadily fixed upon the facts of nature and so receiving their images simply as they are" (Bacon quoted in Alpers, p. 82).

Alpers argues that this interest in the visual in Dutch culture led the artist and microscopist to perceive the world in a similar way, with emphasis on what she calls multiplying, dividing and opening. By multiplying, she means interest in the innumerable small elements within a larger body or the differences between individuals of a single species; dividing means seeing an enlargement of a small part of a larger body; and opening means revealing the inside of objects or organisms. The exquisite detail in the Dutch art of this time and the interest in texture and minute detail are all manifestations of these processes, which were obviously also important to a microscopist like van Leeuwenhoek. I should note that the drawings of sperm and bacteria and protozoa that van Leeuwenhoek is famous for were done by a "visual scribe" whom he employed to record his observations, so he did not trust Hinchman's approach to the visual world.

Conclusion

In *On Seeing Nature,* a very environmentally conscious book on looking at the living world, Steven Meyers (1987) argues that "consciously selecting specific problems, and finding pleasure in the process of learning to see, constitute a large part of aesthetic vision and help to keep both seeing and wonder alive" (p. 104). He thinks that learning to find pleasure in the process of seeing is part of developing the ability to see nature. I think it's important for us to keep this idea in mind as we introduce students to the visual richness of biology. It is easy to become sated by the vast number of beautiful organisms and wonderful views of nature. It is also easy to get so bogged down in helping students to understand the sometimes difficult concepts of biology, the concepts that lie beneath the visual richness, that this richness is forgotten. It might be a good idea to have students simply look at a peanut or a leaf or a flower. Georgia O'Keeffe said that she first became interested in drawing flowers when a grade school teacher passed them just to look at them. For O'Keeffe this opened up a whole new world of wonder, one she never tired of exploring during the almost hundred years of her life. While few of us can hope to produce future O'Keeffes, I think encouraging our students to explore the pleasures of seeing may add something to their lives and may also make them better biologists.

Note: I would like to thank Douglas Burton-Christie for sharing his article with me and Julie Upton for giving me Hannah Hinchman's book. Also, many of the ideas in this article were developed during my stay at Vassar College during the 1997 National Endowment for the Humanities Summer Institute on "The Environmental Imagination."

References

Alpers, S. (1983). *The Art of Describing: Dutch Art in the Seventeenth Century.* Chicago: University of Chicago Press.

Arnheim, R. (1974). *Art and Visual Perception* (2nd ed.). Berkeley, CA: University of California Press.

Burroughs, J. (1981). *Signs and Seasons.* New York: Harper & Row.

Burroughs, J. (1992). *Birch Browsings.* New York: Penguin.

Burton-Christie, D. (1996). Learning to see: Epiphany in the ordinary. *Weavings, 11*(6), 6-15.

Dillard, A. (1974). *Pilgrim at Tinker Creek.* New York: Harper's Magazine Press.

Elkins, J. (1992). On visual desperation and the bodies of protozoa. *Representations, 40,* 33-56.

Elkins, J. (1996). *The Object Stares Back.* New York: Simon & Schuster.

Hacking, I. (1981). Do we see through a microscope? *Pacific Philosophical Quarterly, 62,* 305-322.

Hinchman, H. (1997). *A Trail Through Leaves: The Journal as a Path to Place.* New York: Norton.

Koch, M. (1992). *Bird Egg Feather Nest.* New York: Stewart, Tabori & Chang.

Krutch, J.W. (1952). *The Desert Year.* New York: Sloane.

Leopold, A. (1953). *Round River.* New York: Oxford University Press.

McKim, R. (1980). *Experiences in Visual Thinking* (2nd ed.). Monterey, CA: Brooks/Cole.

McLean, M.A. (1987). *Mary Anne's Garden: Drawings and Writings.* New York: Abrams.

Meyers, S. (1987). *On Seeing Nature.* Boulder, CO: Fulcrum.

Perkins, D. (1994). *The Intelligent Eye: Learning to Think by Looking at Art*. Santa Monica, CA: Getty Center for Education in the Arts.

Ruestow, E. (1996). *The Microscope in the Dutch Republic*. Cambridge, Great Britain: Cambridge University Press.

Watts, M.T. (1975). *Reading the Landscape of America* (2nd ed.). New York: Macmillan.

D'Arcy Thompson's Ice Cream

In his memorial essay on the great morphologist D'Arcy Thompson, the ecologist Evelyn Hutchinson writes that he only met Thompson once, when Thompson visited Yale and they both attended a staff meeting at the Osborn Zoological Laboratory. Since it was the birthday of one of the professors, someone had sent out for ice cream and "no one present is likely to forget the Olympian gusto with which the author of *On Growth and Form* disposed of his portion" (p. 170). I like this story because I think it says a great deal about two biologists whom I admire. At the time, Thompson was in his mid-70s and his zest for eating ice cream mirrored his zest for biology. At home in Scotland, he was working on the revisions for the second edition of his Olympian *On Growth and Form* (1942), a study of the relationship between mathematics and biological form. As far as Hutchinson is concerned, that he would mention ice cream in Thompson's obituary indicates that he had a sense of humor, and it also indicates that he saw the importance of such a piece of biographical information that can only be characterized as trivial. Mentioning D'Arcy Thompson's eating ice cream was Hutchinson's way of saying that even

My dear Miss Arber,
y dear Mrs. Arber,
dearest Agnes,
dear Mrs. Arber,

larger-than-life figures in science are human beings with all their complexities, inconsistencies and foibles.

In my mind Thompson's ice cream goes alongside a number of other epiphanies. Hutchinson himself has a long passage in his autobiography (1979) about the periodic liquefaction of the blood of Saint Januarius in a reliquary in Naples, not the ordinary topic of interest for an eminent freshwater ecologist. Another example of such trivia is in the autobiography of the entomologist and ecologist Edward O. Wilson (1994): he mentions that when he was teaching at Harvard and doing field studies on islands off the coast of Florida he made the trip by train because his wife didn't want him to fly any more than he absolutely had to until their daughter reached high school age. This item made me look at Wilson in a new light. He has been a controversial figure in biology at least since the publication of his *Sociobiology* in 1975. He is a vocal advocate for the idea that there is a genetic basis to human behavior, a concept that many see leading in dangerous directions: to eugenics and criminal punishments based on biological destiny. Though in more recent years he has shifted the focus of his energies to preservation of rain forests and thus of biodiversity, I was always a little leery of Wilson because of sociobiology. But when I read about his train trips, my attitude toward him softened. He might have some radical ideas about human behavior, but his own behavior smacked of very traditional family values.

I've collected any number of such stories about biologists as human beings. There is the biochemist Arthur Kornberg (1989) dedicating his autobiography to the memory of his wife Sylvie, his "great discovery." And there is the physiologist Homer Smith (1953) dedicating his book on the evolution of the kidney to his wife and young son, and then adding, on a separate page, a dedication to Blitz, the laboratory dog whom Smith describes later in the book as "the cooperative subject of renal research" for 12 years. There is the molecular biologist Mahlon Hoagland (1990) admitting in his autobiography his lifetime habit of doing sculpture alongside science, and there is Alexander Fleming's hobby of "painting" pictures by smearing agar with cultures of variously colored microorganisms, and checking them at daily intervals to see how they "developed" as the colonies grew larger and the colors became more distinct (Ludovici 1952). I could go on and mention Lewis Thomas' (1983) fascination with the results of an experiment with rabbits in which their ears wilted; Louis Pasteur's cleaning of his knife and fork before he ate (Dubos 1950); the developmental biologist John Tyler Bonner's (1993) chagrin when his lecture on form in plant life and its relationship to Goethe's botany and to

Naturphilosophie was met with this question from one of his students: "How long would it take to die if one cut someone's jugular vein?" (p. 99)

But I have to stop. There is an endless number of stories like this, and on face value, they don't seem very useful. What difference does it make if Evelyn Hutchinson was fascinated by religious relics or Edward Wilson took the bus? These facts have nothing to do with the biology these men developed. But I do think these items have some interest because they show the human-ness of these biologists. Knowing these facts somehow makes it easier to appreciate that biology is done by human beings, that it is more than a mass of information in a textbook. While I am interested in the latest developments in molecular biology and ecology, I also have a craving to know more about the people who do biology. Recently, I had an opportunity to learn more about the lives of two of my favorite biologists. One is a botanist, Agnes Arber, about whom I've written previously (1995), and the other is that dessert-lover, D'Arcy Thompson.

When Arber died in 1960, her daughter, the geologist Muriel Arber, had her mother's papers sent to the Hunt Institute for Botanical Documentation at Carnegie Mellon University in Pittsburgh. When I wrote to the Hunt Institute asking for information on its holdings on Arber, one item on the list I received stood out: letters between Arber and D'Arcy Thompson. I couldn't wait to see what two of my favorite biologists had to say to each other. When I visited the Hunt Institute, I found that the Arber collection is interesting for what it has as well as for what it lacks. There is a large number of letters — well over a hundred — preserved there, but most of them were written to Arber rather than by her. There are a few drafts of letters by Arber, cases where she was obviously rehearsing a response to a particularly difficult piece of criticism of her work, or in at least one case, the typing job was so poor that she must have decided to stay over and type a clean copy. But for the most part, the letters in the collection were written to Arber.

D'Arcy Thompson

For the correspondence with D'Arcy Thompson, there is unfortunately almost nothing at the Hunt of Arber's letters to him, though his letters, which carefully reply to what she wrote in hers, do indirectly give some flavor of what she must have been writing to him. Their correspondence apparently began in 1917 when she wrote to comment on a few points in his recently published *On Growth and Form*. She must have taken issue with some of his observations and suggested recent botanical literature that he might want to investigate. In 1917 Thompson was 57 years old and

Arber 38. They would correspond off and on for the next 30 years until shortly before his death in 1948. In his first letter to her, Thompson addresses her as "My dear Miss Arber," but she must have let him know that she was a married woman. Because from then on she is "My dear Mrs. Arber" until close to the end of their correspondence when she becomes "My dearest Agnes" in just one letter, but then reverts to Mrs. Arber in subsequent ones.

In his first letter, Thompson shows himself to be a charmer: admitting that she may have a point about the issues she raises, but turning some of her comments around by stating that his tendency is to discount what's taken as the traditional wisdom. He writes that he will investigate the recent research she cites, but then suggests that she should investigate some history. While we don't have her reply, we can assume that she let him know, very engagingly I'm sure, that she was in fact in the habit of investigating history. She had published a history of herbals in 1912 and had also published articles on such botanical notables as Nehemiah Grew (1906) and Guy de la Brosse (1913).

Over the years, Thompson and Arber sent each other articles they wrote when they thought the other might be interested in the topic involved. Thompson sent condolences in 1918 when Arber's husband, the paleobotanist Newell Arber, died. In a much later letter, he referred to Arber's daughter Muriel as "the lassie" and hoped that she wasn't too perturbed by the mistakes she came across while reading his book which he referred to as "G.F." In the 1940s, he was in his 80s and was busily preparing a second edition of G.F. At this time, he wrote a newsy letter about articles he had come across, and then, when he had finished typing the letter, it struck him that Arber might be of help to him, so he added a handwritten postscript. He needed two illustrations for the book, and needed them quickly. His regular illustrator was busy having a baby, perhaps Arber could do the work. Could she please let him know by return post if she would be willing to do him this favor.

Arber was the daughter of the professional artist, Henry Robert Robertson, who began giving her art lessons when she was eight years old. At the Hunt is a sketchbook of beautiful watercolors of flowers — botanical illustrations — that Arber did in her teens; they are evidence that her father had indeed taught her well. She did all the illustrations for her articles and books, and in an earlier letter, Thompson had praised her drawings as being among the best examples of botanical illustration and very much influenced by the Japanese style, which I think refers to their sparseness and grace. So as he finished his letter, Thompson must have suddenly realized that he had a skilled artist right underneath his nose who could help him with his illustrations. And naturally, Arber replied that she'd be happy to oblige, though she wasn't sure that she could do a good job on material that wasn't familiar to her.

Thompson sent Arber a bird pelvis he wanted drawn — with the two faces marked A and B, explaining that he wanted the pelvis drawn from the A side, with the pelvis slightly tilted to reveal part of the B side. Thompson also enclosed a sketch in brown paper, indicating generally what he was looking for. Always the charmer, he admitted that while he could draw the pelvis on a blackboard, he became incompetent when it came to drawing on paper. I'm sure at this point Arber was having second thoughts about the whole project, but she made the drawing and sent it off within a week — after all, in the letter that accompanied the drawing, Thompson had again reminded her that time was of the essence.

But then several weeks went by, and Arber heard nothing from him. She seemed to have little confidence in her drawing skills — at least when it came to avian anatomy. When she could no longer stand the suspense, she finally wrote Thompson, reassuring him that she would not take offense if her drawing was inadequate. He quickly wrote back, apologizing for his delay in writing and explaining that it had absolutely nothing to do with her drawing, which was indeed more than adequate. The problem was that he had been suffering from a terrible eye inflammation which made it impossible for him to work, and though several medicines were tried, none did the least bit of good. Finally, his doctor "had a brain-wave, the last thing I expected of him" and suggested that the problem might be an allergic reaction to some new plants Thompson's wife had brought home. "Banishing" them from the house did the trick. Thompson went on to reassure Arber that "your drawing will be exactly right when it is finished." But less than two weeks later, he is urging her to send the drawing back to him "shaded or not! I am more than half amused at your distrust of your own powers, for I know you can draw very well." He enclosed a rubbing of violet leaves that he also wanted drawn,"... unshaded. This you will do without the least trouble — *quickly, please.*"

These letters are what could be called a footnote to history. They do not contain any significant information about either Thompson or Arber, but reading them was nonetheless an exciting experience for me. I know about each of these individuals, primarily from their published writings. Thompson's massive *On Growth and Form* (1942) and Arber's slim *The Mind and the Eye* (1954), a study of the philosophy of biology, are two of my favorite books. What makes each of these books so memorable is not only the beautiful writing style of each author, but also the way their enthusiasm and passion for their subject infuse their writing. It is evident in these books that the authors are remarkable people and it has been wonderful getting to know them a little better through their correspondence. Here are two people whom I would like to be able to spend time with. While this is physically impossible, these letters are the next best thing, and I feel very fortunate that I had the opportunity to read them.

Other Letters – and the War

Among the few letters at the Hunt written by Arber, there are several to the botanist B.C. Sharman, a botanist of the University of Leeds who contributed these letters to the Hunt. In one letter Arber tells of how she had acquired a teasel specimen Sharman had requested. She had written to the superintendent of the Cambridge University Botanic Garden several weeks earlier to ask his permission to cut a pod, but had never received a reply. In the meantime, she had visited the garden and found a promising specimen, but it needed a few more weeks to ripen and dry. When what she considered adequate time had elapsed, she visited the garden again and failed to find the superintendent in his office, however "the teasel had so obviously ceased to be an ornamental object, that I appropriated it."

There are also a couple of letters Arber wrote in the late 1940s to the California botanist Edgar Anderson, author of the wonderful book *Plants, Man and Life* (1952). Anderson had visited Arber's home in Cambridge shortly after World War II and must have been impressed by the strict food rationing the British were still experiencing, so he sent food packages to Arber and her daughter on at least two occasions. Arber wrote beautifully warm letters of thank you detailing how each of the items Anderson and his wife had included in the packages would be useful and delicious. She admitted that she would never be as good a cook as Mrs. Anderson because "alas, I only began cooking in my sixtieth year (when we dispensed with service, a year before the outbreak of war, when things were getting critical) and I fear I shall never be really expert." I should also note that Arber rented a house that was not wired for electricity until after her death, so not only did she come to cooking late in life, but under less than ideal conditions – primitive equipment, and rationing to boot.

As Arber's letters to Anderson indicate, she and her daughter were affected by World War II – as was everyone in Britain. Not only did this mean that she had to learn to cook and spend time doing all manner of household chores instead of pursuing research, but laboratory supplies were difficult to come by, so she shifted her focus away from morphological studies toward more historical and philosophical work, publishing *The Natural Philosophy of Plant Form* in 1950. She also had to put up with air raids, and in the letter about the teasel she tells Sharman of a bomb that landed in the street outside her home. It didn't break any windows, but a piece of flying debris broke through the roof and a rainstorm the next day wreaked havoc in the Arber residence.

It is obvious from some of the newspaper clippings she kept that she closely followed the bombing destruction in London as well. In particular, she saved several clippings related to raids on the night of December 30, 1941, when eight churches designed by the great architect Christopher Wren were demolished. On each of the clippings, she underlined the remarks about St. Mary's Church Newgate. I assumed that this might have been the church where she was married or where her family had worshiped, so its destruction was particularly upsetting to her, but later, going through a file of postcards, I found one with a photograph taken in 1950 of the remains of St. Mary's Church Newgate. Grass is growing up through what is left of the floor, there is no roof, and only parts of the walls remain. But intact on a pedestal is a memorial to the botanist Nehemiah Grew — whom Arber had written about years before. So that's why St. Mary's Church was so important to her; its significance was botanical rather than personal.

What's Missing

In a letter to the director of the Hunt Institute at the time she sent her mother's papers there, Muriel Arber noted that a few years earlier her mother had gone through her papers and thrown out a good deal that she considered would be of no value to anyone. I'm really sorry she did that. I loved going through the letters and clippings Arber saved, and look forward to spending more time going through the nearly 20 notebooks preserved at the Hunt, even though Arber's handwriting is less than easy to decipher. But the more I sifted through her papers, the more obvious it became that there is also a lot missing. There are, for example, no personal letters, no letters from family members. I would love to see letters that her husband had written her; or her daughter who traveled to Dorset during World War II to continue her geological work while her mother remained in Cambridge; or letters from her sister, Janet Robertson, an artist with whom she might have discussed problems in illustration. There is also almost no correspondence concerning publications. All her books except her last one, *The Manifold and the One* (1957), were published by

Cambridge University Press, and there must have been a great deal involved in their production, particularly because most are profusely illustrated. Also, none of the originals of the hundreds of illustrations she did for her books is there, though at the end of my stay, I did get a glimpse of related material.

The archivist of the Hunt Institute, Anita Karg, couldn't have been nicer to me during my stay. She had all the materials out and organized when I arrived, and when other members of the Hunt staff visited her office, she made it a point to introduce me to them. That's how I met James White, Director of Art for the Hunt Institute. When he heard I was working on Arber, he mentioned that there were a few of her drawings in his collection and asked if I would like to see them. I jumped at the chance and went upstairs to the art archives, another amazing part of the Hunt. What White showed me was a small notebook with pen-and-ink drawings pasted into its pages — 12 drawings in all. Some of the drawings have notes around them written on the notebook page.

So in finding still another piece of material on Arber, I uncovered another mystery: why were these drawings preserved here? She must have done a large number of drawings over the years in preparation for the drawings that went into her publications. What happened to all of them? Were they among the papers she destroyed as worthless? Asking myself questions like this makes me realize how difficult and frustrating, even heartbreaking, a historian's job can be. Biologists get frustrated when the organism they're working on won't yield the information they are looking for, when experiments fail time and again, when the instruments available don't have the power to do the necessary job demanded of them. But obviously, we don't have a corner on the frustration market. Being married to a historian for 17 years should have made me aware of all of this, but there's no substitute for direct experience. Despite the holes in the Arber collection, there is enough at the Hunt to keep me busy for a long time if I decide to delve deeper into Arber's life and work.

Before I end, there is one more item at the Hunt that I want to mention. It is in the "ice cream" category, something not very significant, but yet telling about a biologist's life. It is a photograph, wonderfully crisp and clear, of eight men in Edwardian suits standing around a beautifully clad woman who is seated. The woman is, of course, Agnes Arber, and the photograph was taken on the roof of the Cambridge botany building. It is dated to about 1912 and is labeled as being the members of the Cambridge Botany Department. The man standing just behind Arber and over her right shoulder is Newell Arber, with his stiff white collar and hair parted in the middle. By this time, he and Agnes were married, and she was working at the Balfour Biological Laboratory for Women, one of the only places at Cambridge where laboratory facilities were open to women (Packer 1997; Richmond 1997). In 1912, Arber's history of herbals was published and within a year their daughter Muriel was born.

While I have seen other pictures of Arber, I particularly like this one for a number of reasons. Most obviously, here is one woman in a very male-dominated environment, a woman who will, more than 30 years later, be only the third woman to become a Fellow of the Royal Society. Also, Arber looks particularly beautiful in this photo. She is looking straight at the camera, a lovely woman in her early 30s, confident of her scientific abilities and happy in her private life.

Finally, I love Arber's outfit. She seems to be dressed all in black or some other dark color, with only a white collar breaking the darkness. She has on a large, wide-brimmed hat with an ostrich plume on one side and a large organdy flower on the other. Her skirt extends to her shoes, and she is carrying an umbrella [this is England] with what appears to be an antler handle. I asked Anita Karg to reproduce this photo so I'd have a memento to bring back from my trip to the Hunt Institute. It's not really as good as the original photo, but I'm learning that delving into the past, like delving into a living organism, involves many compromises. You do the best you can with the resources available to you, all the time relishing the wonderful experiences that are available.

Note: I would like to thank Anita Karg at the Hunt Institute for all her help and patience. Also, this article was written while I was on a research leave, and I am grateful to St. John's University for this support.

References

Anderson, E. (1952). *Plants, Man and Life*. Berkeley, CA: University of California Press.

Arber, A. (1906). Nehemiah Grew and the study of plant anatomy. *Science Progress-London, 1,* 150-158.

Arber, A. (1912). *Herbals: Their Origin and Evolution*. Cambridge, Great Britain: Cambridge University Press.

Arber, A. (1913). The botanical philosophy of Guy de la Brosse: A study in seventeenth-century thought. *Isis, 1,* 359-369.

Arber, A. (1950). *The Natural Philosophy of Plant Form*. Cambridge, Great Britain: Cambridge University Press.

Arber, A. (1954). *The Mind and the Eye: A Study of the Biologist's Standpoint*. Cambridge, Great Britain: Cambridge University Press.

Arber, A. (1957). *The Manifold and the One.* London: John Murray.

Bonner, J.T. (1993). *Life Cycles: Reflections of an Evolutionary Biologist.* Princeton, NJ: Princeton University Press.

Dubos, R. (1950). *Louis Pasteur: Free Lance of Science.* New York: Scribner's.

Flannery, M. (1995). Goethe and Arber: Unity in diversity. *The American Biology Teacher, 57,* 544-547.

Hoagland, M. (1990). *Toward the Habit of Truth: A Life in Science.* New York: Norton.

Hutchinson, G.E. (1953). *The Itinerant Ivory Tower: Scientific and Literary Essays.* New Haven, CT: Yale University Press.

Hutchinson, G.E. (1953). *The Kindly Fruits of the Earth: Recollections of an Embryo Ecologist.* New Haven, CT: Yale University Press.

Kornberg, A. (1989). *For the Love of Enzymes: The Odyssey of a Biochemist.* Cambridge, MA: Harvard University Press.

Ludovici, L.J. (1952). *Fleming: Discovery of Penicillin.* London: Andrew Dakers.

Packer, K. (1997). A laboratory of one's own: The life and works of Agnes Arber, F.R.S. (1879-1960). *Notes and Records of the Royal Society of London, 51*(1), 87-104.

Richmond, M. (1997). "A Lab of One's Own": The Balfour Biological Laboratory for Women at Cambridge University, 1884-1914. *Isis, 83*(3), 422-455.

Smith, H.W. (1953). *From Fish to Philosopher.* Boston: Little, Brown.

Thomas, L. (1983). *The Youngest Science: Notes of a Medicine-Watcher.* New York: Viking.

Thompson, D. (1942). *On Growth and Form* (2nd ed.). Cambridge, Great Britain: Cambridge University Press.

Wilson, E.O. (1975). *Sociobiology: The New Synthesis.* Cambridge, MA: Harvard University Press.

Wilson, E.O. (1994). *Naturalist.* Washington, DC: Island Press.

Dressing in Style?
An Essay on
the Lab Coat

Every Sunday, I take a look at the Style section of *The New York Times*, not because I want to keep up on the latest in the fashion world – I'm not really into very short skirts or tattoos – but because I'm addicted to the "Vows" column where each week they describe a particularly romantic nuptial. Last fall, as I was all set to turn to this feature, my eye was caught by something on the first page of the section: a man in a lab coat. What was he doing there amidst extremely thin models and men in spiky hair? The title of the article hinted at the answer: "No Germs on the Runway: Lab Chic." It was a report on one of the latest trends in the fashion world: the clean, laboratory look. This came as quite a surprise to me, but it seems that it is a logical extension of the spare, minimalist fashion of the 90s. As David Colman (1998) notes in this article, the minimalist look has been described as clean, and "you can't get much cleaner than a lab coat" (p. 9-1). He suggests that there are also other reasons for this interest in white clothes that offer little in the way of decoration but a lot in the way of protection. Looking very much like what one would wear in a clean room in Silicon Valley, they symbolize safety and order and provide an easy way to suggest high technology.

About a year earlier, *The New York Times* ran a very different kind of article on white coats: about how doctors and other medical personnel are using them less and less. Abigail Zuger (1997) describes how many patients' symptoms worsen when confronted by a white-coated figure. This effect has been studied and measured in a number of cases to the point where there are recognizable syndromes: "white-coat hypertension" and "white-coat hyperglycemia." Because of such effects, some doctors have taken to wearing street clothes when seeing patients, and nurses and other medical workers often wear brightly colored uniforms. But Zuger writes that there are also problems with this tack because of something called "white-coat compliance," where some patients more readily obey orders if they are given by a figure dressed in a white coat. The continuing importance of the white coat in medicine is also indicated by the fact that over the past few years many medical schools have begun a ritual called the "white coat ceremony" in which first-year medical students don this symbol of the profession.

DAST

I mention these two articles because they say something about the part dress plays in defining work roles and because they also reflect aspects of the myth and reality of the lab coat at the end of the 20th century. It may be considered passé by many within the scientific and medical communities, but at the same time it is still seen as a very powerful symbol of science by the public at large. For a number of years, I've been giving students in a course I teach on science and technology the DAST or Draw-A-Scientist-Test on the first day of the semester. It is a very simple, perhaps even simple-minded, test devised by David Wade Chambers (1983) of Deakin University in Australia. While this test was designed for elementary school students, it works well with my students too, though I'm sure I get more groans than teachers of younger students would.

To administer DAST, I simply give out sheets of white paper and ask students to draw a scientist. I give no more instructions than this, and after about 10 minutes I always have very interesting results, results that are usually frighteningly similar to those Chambers obtained. The majority of students draw males wearing lab coats. Often these men wear glasses and have facial hair; in some cases they are also bald. Whether the wearer is male or female, she or he is usually dressed in a lab coat, often complete with nerd pack. The individual is frequently holding a piece of laboratory glassware like a beaker or test tube, or such equipment is displayed on a table or lab bench — where there might also be that other ubiquitous symbol of science: the microscope. Chambers found that usually at least one person in a class will draw what he terms "an alternative stereotype," meaning a mad scientist-type figure, often with wild hair, and sometimes even fangs, and carrying a bubbling flask. I get similar results with at least a couple of students taking this approach.

I do this exercise because it is a great way to get at students' assumptions about science: that science is an essentially male domain, that there can be something weird and scary about science, and that the lab coat is an almost universal signifier of science. This is despite the fact that many scientists rarely if ever wear lab coats, particularly today, when — as in the case of medical professionals — many have abandoned this piece of apparel as being pretentious and unnecessary. When I started college in 1965, buying a lab coat was a sign that I was taking a "real" science course, but it was also a practical necessity. What it looked like after I finished general chemistry was indicative of this. I went to an institution with a strict dress code; slacks weren't allowed until 1968, and I shudder to think of what would have happened to a student who showed up in jeans. While acid burns now may make jeans more desirable, they would definitely have not improved a good wool dress.

In general over the past 30 years, there has been a move toward more informality and less emphasis on outward signs of status. Yet the lab coat isn't dead; it has just moved into the fashion world. It seems that as the lab coat's practical importance has decreased, its symbolic significance has grown. Fashion designers use it as a shorthand for technology, while others use it to indicate a scientific attitude, as in the title of an article in *Entrepreneur* magazine's guide to franchise and business opportunities: "Put on Your White Lab Coat: A Little Research Before You Buy an Opportunity Can Mean the Difference Between Success and Failure" (Caffey 1994). Here donning a lab coat doesn't mean going into a science-related business. But rather taking a scientific attitude toward researching business opportunities: being systematic, logical and objective. In the children's story, *Lab Coat Girl* (Palatini 1999), Trudie decides to perform experiments in order to discover the reason behind her friend Ben's unusual reactions to foods. The lab coat Trudie wears indicates that she is serious about this research and that what she is doing is real science.

Obviously, the fact that a girl takes the lead in the investigation is an effort to provide a role model for girls attracted to science careers, and it is interesting that the lab coat is used as a symbol of entry into science.

Forerunners of the Lab Coat

There is really a great deal behind this idea of a female entering science and taking up the dress as well as the research styles and approaches of male scientists. To do this idea full justice requires a look into the history of the lab coat as well as the history of women in science. The lab coat as we know it is essentially a 20th-century invention, but stereotypical dress in science has a much longer history than that. There are any number of paintings in which an alchemist is pictured wearing a robe tied with cord, an outfit that would protect the wearer from the strong chemicals used in alchemy. Such a robe, as does the modern-day lab coat, signifies a person who is set off from the ordinary. The fact that the robe resembles that worn by the members of some religious orders implies a similarity between the clergy and scientists: both are fervently committed to the pursuit of truth, and both are set apart from the average layperson.

By the 19th century, the bathrobe-like garment had given way to aprons and shop coats in blue or beige, but the costume depended as much on the social status of the scientific worker as on the need for protection. In France in particular, bourgeois gentlemen who were interested in science had a problem. Research was often dirty work, so how could one retain one's symbols of class – and yet do real research? One solution was to let others do the dirty work. In an engraving of a laboratory during the early days of the Pasteur Institute in the late 1880s, there are two types of dress evident. Those working at the laboratory benches have aprons on, while those overseeing the work are in the typical bourgeois frock coat. Clearly, the people in charge – the thinkers – are not the doers. But not all scientists took this tack. The painter Leon Lhermitte portrayed Claude Bernard doing a dissection. Bernard is wearing typical bourgeois clothing, but he has his suit covered with a large, white apron, and the blood stains covering it indicate that the protection was certainly needed.

Women's Dress and Field Biology

The same kind of class concerns are found in images of women doing science in the 19th century. The difficulty of collecting specimens is indicated in William Dyce's painting, *Pegwell Bay, Kent: A Recollection of October 5, 1858*: upper-class women, the only ones who would have had the time for such endeavors, seem to find it difficult enough in their long, wide skirts to bend over to pick up specimens on a rocky beach; wading into the water or climbing the cliffs in the background would be out of the question. Darwin's granddaughter Gwen Raverat (1952), in her memoir of her childhood in Cambridge, describes the layers of clothes worn by a typical young lady in the late 19th century. "Beginning at the bottom, or scratch" (p. 264) with thick, long-legged, long-sleeved woolen combinations, she lists 14 items, including three petticoats. Considering this list, it is no wonder that it wasn't thought possible for women to participate in most types of biological fieldwork.

Though natural history was a popular 19th-century pastime, particularly in Great Britain, there were definite limits to women's involvement. Elizabeth Keeney (1992) describes how women survived botanizing in full-length skirts and genteel shoes:

> The answer to the quandary of what to wear comes from differences between male and female behavior in the field: many female botanizers solved the dilemma of how to botanize and be genteel at the same time by restricting their collecting to very 'tame' situations, or by recruiting males to collect for them (p. 77).

While some women borrowed clothes from male relatives or wore the reform or "Bloomer" outfit, others simply gave up and had other people collect for them or bought specimens from commercial suppliers. Even in the first half of the 20th century, dress was a problem for women field biologists. In a photograph of corn geneticist and Nobel Prize winner Barbara McClintock taken in 1929, she is wearing an outfit similar to those of her male colleagues — shirt, knickers, sweater and oxford shoes — something that was considered inappropriate by many of the women of the day. In her biography of McClintock, Evelyn Fox Keller (1983) writes that when McClintock was a graduate student:

> she decided that she could not work in the cornfields wearing dresses and skirts that other women wore. Off she went to the tailor and ordered a pair of knickers, or 'plus fours' as they were then called. It was a question of what I could live with, and I couldn't live with the costumes that others had in the past (p. 34).

Thus, in the case of fieldwork, clothing was more than incidental. It severely impacted how women could do research. If they used specimens obtained by others, this restricted both what they could study and how much they could learn about the specimens because they had little feel for the environment from which the specimens were collected. Or they had to content themselves with specimens that they could collect themselves, but without too much strenuous activity. In these cases, the extent of their studies was determined not by intellectual curiosity, but by practicality. Thus, besides the societal constraints that prevented women from pursuing careers in science, their clothes themselves militated against involvement in such careers.

Class and Clothing

But if 19th-century dress caused problems for women who were interested in science, there were also problems for men as well. Upper and middle-class men were expected to wear suits and ties at all times. Casual dress was unheard of. If some activity could not be pursued in such attire, then perhaps it wasn't something a gentleman should be involved in. There is a painting in the Metropolitan Museum of Art that I love. It is a portrait of a chemist named Thomas Price painted by Henry Alexander in 1887. Price is seated at this workbench surrounded by all kinds of glassware; it is a DAST drawing gone wild — except for the fact that Price is wearing a jacket and tie, no lab coat. The lab coat is a product of the marriage of science and medicine, and its invention had to wait for the establishment of sanitary practices in medicine. The lab coat is also the product of combining two 19th-century pieces of laboratory wear: the apron and the shop coat.

As the painting of Claude Bernard indicates, the apron was a nice compromise between no protective covering at all and a more enshrouding shop coat, the kind that factory workers, artisans and shopkeepers often wore. Such coats — usually gray blue or beige in color, but rarely white because they were worn by the lower classes who had to be practical — were not appropriate for the bourgeois scientist. The apron was much more fitting since it did not completely hide the clothing that was such an important symbol of class, yet it offered some protection against being soiled in the lab. Perhaps the incompleteness of the protection also implied that the wearer was affluent enough to replace any garment that became hopelessly stained, and thus didn't have to resort to the very protective shop coat; only people who worried about money had to cover up so completely.

By the early 20th-century, it was not uncommon for laboratory workers to wear protective coats. For example there is a 1909 photograph of a laboratory in the Rockefeller Institute in which everyone is wearing a coat, but still, these are not the typical lab coats of today. The color is wrong; it is either gray or blue, but certainly not white. Yet the color makes a lot of sense. Why wear a white coat that shows every stain, when a dark coat will show less dirt? This is a very practical point which any homemaker would make, yet scientists seem to have ignored this good advice and traded in their brown or blue coats for white ones. How and why did the change occur? I think the answer relates to the changes that have taken place in medical garb.

Medicine and the White Coat

In his 1875 painting, *The Gross Clinic,* Thomas Eakins portrays the surgeon Samuel Gross operating on a boy's leg. Both Gross and his assistants are wearing street clothes. Though the patient is covered in white sheets, there is no other white in the painting. This is in marked contrast to Eakin's 1899 work, *The Agnew Clinic,* in which Dr. D. Hayes Agnew and his assistants are completely covered in white clothes that are obviously meant to be worn in the operating theater and not on the street. In the 24 years between these two paintings, medicine had undergone a revolution. The proselytizing of Lister, Pasteur and others had brought sterile procedure to the operating rooms and changed ideas of sanitation in all areas of medicine. But that didn't mean that white became the color of choice for laboratory scientists as well as for physicians. This change in haberdashery didn't occur until the 20th century.

When, as in *The Agnew Clinic,* white became the symbol of cleanliness in surgical procedure, this relationship between white and sanitary conditions soon spread to other areas of medicine: nurses' uniforms changed from gray or black to white, and doctors took to wearing white coats when visiting patients as well as when operating. This trend in medicine coincided with the introduction of more laboratories in hospitals, both for microbiological and pathological testing, and for research. In other words, medicine became more scientific, and with the movement of science – and scientists – into hospital settings, it is not surprising that the scientists soon took to wearing the same white coats as the doctors. This was not only for efficiency – why have more than one type of coat used in one facility – it was also a way for scientists to gain status in the medical community. Many doctors looked down on laboratory workers as being of less importance than physicians in the medical setting. By dressing like doctors, the scientists sought to overcome their second-class citizenship. This is another indication that the clothing of scientists, like a great deal of other clothing, can become a class symbol. I suspect the rise of another institution may also have played a role here, and that is the development of large commercial laundries that could keep hospitals and other research institutions stocked with sparkling white coats without any work on the part of the wearers.

As science became more professionalized in the 20th century, more and more scientists moved to wearing white lab coats, and the blue and brown coats were only seen on the backs of machinists, glass washers and technicians. The aura of superiority associated with the white coat in medical settings now cast its glow on many types of research institutions. And it became de rigueur for scientists to be pictured in their lab coats. These portrayals became so common that the lab coat became a powerful symbol of science — in the minds of children, fashion designers, and the public at large. And it remains so today, even as many medical personnel shed their white coats as intimidating, and as brightly colored and even tie-dyed lab coats become available. Lab coats, from the practical point of view, are a lot less necessary today than they were in the past since T-shirts and jeans have replaced more formal dress. I have heard of at least one lab where the only time coats are worn is for photographs.

The Spotless Lab Coat

Before I close, I want to mention two more paintings of lab-coated figures that illustrate points about the symbolic power of lab coats. One is a straightforward portrait and the other a more complex work. The portrait, by Betsy Graves Reneau, is of the noted African-American physician and researcher Charles Rich Drew, who played a large role in improving blood preservation methods during World War II (Love 1996). In describing the painting, William Gerdts (1981) notes that Drew's "white laboratory coat is spotless; for the medical man purity of costume symbolizes perfectionism and purity of motivation" (p. 89). I think the word "medical" could be changed to "scientific" because the sentence could be equally true to people's attitudes toward scientists, and this is a bit daunting. Purity and perfectionism are tough rows to hoe, and it may be that the promise of the white coat has not always been made good on, which is why there is a prevalent distrust of scientists among the public, why some of the scientists produced by DAST-takers have smoke rising from their ears or fangs coming out of their mouths. In a portrait of an African-American physician/researcher, the white coat takes on added significance besides its symbolism of science as a world apart and as a superior way of thinking. Here the white coat is also signifying that an African-American has been accepted into this rarefied atmosphere, that he has arrived.

The other painting I want to mention is a rather ambiguous one. In *The Innocent Eye Test,* Mark Tansey has a cow standing in a museum gallery and staring at a painting of two cows. Like much of Tansey's work, this is a commentary on modern art and art criticism, and specifically on the question of how those with no knowledge of art, those with innocent eyes, view a painting. But I think it is also a commentary on modern science: there are six men in this painting, which is done entirely in shades of gray. One of these men is wearing a lab coat and is taking notes, indicating that this eye test is, indeed, scientific. But there is something strange about this man. Of all the figures in this work, human and bovine, he is the only one who has part of his face obscured. The lower half of his face is blank, as if covered by a surgical mask, yet it is not clear that he is wearing such a mask.

This figure brings to mind a quote from the feminist critic of science, Ruth Bleier (1988), who notes that:

> it is the lab coat, literally and symbolically, that wraps the scientist in the robe of innocence – of a pristine and aseptic neutrality – and gives him, like the klansman, a faceless authority that his audience can't challenge. From that sheeted figure comes a powerful, mysterious, impenetrable, coercive, anonymous male voice (p. 62).

This is a rather strong indictment of a piece of clothing, and it is couched in words that are designed to be inflammatory. But despite the strident rhetorical tone, Bleier is making a legitimate point. The lab coat can be seen not only as a symbol of science, but of masculine science; at the very least, it disguises the gender of its wearer.

As women have become more involved in science, they have become more involved in its trappings, signified by the number of female as well as male scientists photographed in lab coats. Women no longer have the problems of dress that plagued 19th-century women interested in science. But in putting on the white lab coat, they have put on more than a protective covering against the dirt and grime of the lab; they have also put on a symbol of a superior way of thinking, of a better way of looking at the world. Thus, in examining the dress of female and male biologists, we are looking at more than the surface: we are examining the power of a symbol to influence people's attitudes toward science and scientists.

References

Bleier, R. (1988). Lab coat: Robe of innocence or klansman's sheet? In T. deLaurentis (Ed.), *Feminist Studies/Critical Studies* (pp. 55-56). New York: Macmillan.

Caffey, A. (1994). Put on your white lab coat: A little research before you buy an opportunity can mean the difference between success and failure. *Entrepreneur,* 22(11), 20.

Chambers, D.W. (1983). Stereotypic images of the scientist: The "draw-a-scientist-test." *Science Education, 67*(2), 255-265.

Colman, D. (1998, October 4). No germs on the runway: Lab chic. *The New York Times,* pp. 9-1, 9-5.).

Gerdts, W. (1981). *The Art of Healing: Medicine and Science in American Art.* Birmingham, AL: Birmingham Museum of Art.

Keeney, E. (1992). *The Botanizers: Amateur Scientists in Nineteenth-Century America.* Chapel Hill, NC: University of North Carolina Press.

Keller, E.F. (1983). *A Feeling for the Organism.* New York: Freeman.

Love, S. (1996). *One Blood: The Death and Resurrection of Charles R. Drew.* Chapel Hill, NC: University of North Carolina Press.

Palatini, M. (1999). *Lab Coat Girl.* New York: Hyperion.

Raverat, G. (1952). *Period Piece: A Cambridge Childhood.* London: Faber & Faber.

Zuger, A. (1997, November 25). Doctor's white coat fits all: Jekyll, Kildare, Medicine Man. *The New York Times,* p. F4.

Waking Up to Dinosaurs

I've never been a fan of dinosaurs, in part because I tend to be a contrary person. If something is popular, I'm not interested in it, and dinosaurs are definitely popular. They are everywhere, from breakfast cereal to T-shirts; even my four-year-old grandson, who is of course exceptionally bright, knows the names of several species. But I couldn't see getting too excited about a group of organisms that aren't even around any more — no matter how large, how fierce, how bizarre they may have been. I originally thought the interest in dinosaurs was a fad, and I would just wait it out. But if dino-mania is a fad, it is definitely more long-lived than most.

Last year I was teaching a Science, Technology and Society course, when a question about dinosaurs came up, a question hardly germane to the topic under discussion. Because I believe that it takes a certain amount of courage for a student to raise her hand in class, I think each question should be treated respectfully. So I answered the question about dinosaurs. That led to another question, so I answered that, and then there was another. The class time melted away in a cascade of questions about dinosaurs, which had absolutely nothing to do with engineering, the day's topic. But I didn't mind because almost for the first time in the semester, this 8 o'clock class was awake, aware and interested. Until this point, they had been one of the deadest groups of students I'd encountered in a long time, and even my best jokes (such as they are), my cleverest activities, my most positive encouragement, didn't seem to stir them. But dinosaurs did.

After that class, I didn't want to let dinosaurs go. I finagled ways to cover a couple of topics using dinosaurs; after all, many of them were feats of engineering. But to discuss dinosaurs intelligently, I had to learn more about them. I had to stop ignoring them. In the process, I haven't become that much of a convert that I want to be an expert, but I've learned enough to have more respect for these beasts and to begin to see why others have found them so fascinating.

I think part of the attraction of dinosaurs is that they are extinct. If they could still be seen and heard and touched, then they wouldn't be quite as interesting. After all, elephants probably make as much noise as many dinosaurs did, and a blue whale is the biggest animal to ever have lived on Earth, yet neither of these animals seems to have gotten as much press as *T. rex*. Stephen Jay Gould quotes a psychologist as saying that the fascination with dinosaurs is due to the fact that they are big, fierce and extinct – they are scary, but safe; no one is going to get trampled by an *Apatosaurus* or ripped to shreds by an *Allosaurus* (Mitchell 1998b).

The Art and Science of Dinosaurs

Not only are dinosaurs extinct, but they've been extinct for a long time – 65 million years or so (Alvarez 1997). This means that a great deal has to be left to the imagination in terms of dinosaur traits and lifestyles. Many of the articles on the most noteworthy dinosaur fossil finds are accompanied by artists' drawings of what these animals might have looked like. Obviously, these drawings are closely based on the physical findings in the fossil record, but that information doesn't take the artist very far. Even for fossils that are considered spectacular because skin or internal organs are preserved, a leap of the imagination is required to go from these remains to what the animal might have looked like when it was alive. Producing such drawings requires close cooperation between scientist and artist – scientific accuracy must be combined with artistic skills – and that's the theme I want to explore in this column.

The first three-dimensional sculptures of dinosaurs were created about a dozen years after the British anatomist Richard Owen first described this group of organisms in 1842. He had reviewed all the fossil reptiles from the Secondary formations and created a major new category, *Dinosauria,* meaning terrible lizard, for the *Iguanodon* and some other forms. The *Iguanodon* was a bipedal, herbivorous dinosaur that could be up to 30 feet long. Huge beasts like the *Iguanodon* caught the public's imagination in Victorian England; the present day isn't the only era to be afflicted with dino-mania. In 1853 George Benjamin Waterhouse Hawkins was hired to construct four life-size dinosaur models to stand outside the Crystal Palace. This famous edifice was moved to Sydenham Park after the 1851 London Exhibition for which it was built. The dinosaurs were placed on an island in the middle of the lake, presumably so they would be safe from molestation by the crowds that visited the park. The sculptures are still there, though the Crystal Palace eventually burned down. After the success of the Sydenham dinosaurs, Hawkins was brought to New York to produce similar figures for a proposed Paleozoic Museum in Central Park. But there were arguments over the expense and religious questions about an exhibit that brought evolution to mind, so Boss Tweed, ever the enlightened politician, had some of his henchmen destroy the sculptures, and the project died.

Dinosaur Images

One of the most famous paintings of dinosaurs is at Yale University's Peabody Museum of Natural History. It was done during World War II by Rudolph Zallinger, who was completing his studies at Yale's School of Fine Arts. The museum's board decided that the dinosaur hall needed to be enlivened. Since there wasn't enough money available to hire a famous artist, a competent one was found. The completed mural, called *The Age of Reptiles,* is 110 feet long and 16 feet high. It provides a sequential view of the story of dinosaurs, though for two reasons this isn't obvious when first looking at the mural. First, the transition from one era to another is seamless; in addition, the sequence moves from right to left, which is counter to most depictions of events occurring over time.

The Age of Reptiles has become almost the quintessential rendering of dinosaurs, and even though it is now well over 50 years old, it doesn't look very dated (Mitchell 1998a). This is, in part, because so many later paintings of dinosaurs were based on Zallinger's work. But a comparison of the mural with some recent dinosaur images indicates that late 20th-century dinosaurs are more colorful, agile and active than their Yale predecessors. One reason for this change is the debate in the 1970s over whether or not dinosaurs were warm-blooded. This issue got paleontologists to reexamine fossils, and they discovered that a common assumption about dinosaurs — that because of their great size they had to be slow, lumbering creatures — might not necessarily be true. That's when dinosaurs began to pick their tails up off the ground and run rather than plod.

The image change was in part based on new evidence: information like the fact that most dinosaur tracks show no evidence of tail dragging. But it was based on a change of emphasis, a change in what evidence was considered important. There was, for example, a greater interest in color. Even with new findings, most decisions about the color of dinosaurs are based on conjecture and artistic license. Some of the best dinosaur images I've seen are in a book by Frank DeCourten (1998) called *Dinosaurs of Utah,* with illustrations by Carel Brest van Kempen. This book has a great deal of information in it, but the art steals the show; it is spectacular. The illustrations produce a very different atmosphere from that created by Zallinger at Yale. It is a sunnier world, with a lot of running and fighting animals. While *The Age of Reptiles* gives an impression of a leisurely, languid world, the Utah dinosaurs are living in a frenetic one. Which of these approaches is correct, or are they both correct? The latter is more likely. The evidence is mounting that dinosaurs were active animals, but whether they were as brightly colored as they are now sometimes rendered is still an open question, and may well remain one. The world of fossils, particularly of those as old as dinosaur fossils, is a dull world in terms of color. There is rarely any hint of coloration.

The basic lack of information makes the artist's job difficult and also essential, but for this work to have scientific validity, there must also be input from scientists. Wonderful examples of this interplay are found in the two-volume set called *Dinosaurs Past and Present* (Czerkas & Olson 1987) produced in conjunction with an exhibition on dinosaurs at the Natural History Museum of Los Angeles County. Though these volumes are slightly dated because dinosaur research is moving so quickly, there is still a great deal of value here, with wonderful articles on everything from making sense of dinosaurs' tracks, to trying to figure out the arrangement of the plates on the back of *Stegosaurus stenops*. Gregory Paul and Stephen Czerkas, who are both paleontologists and artists, have contributions that deal with how their scientific training influences the decisions they make as artists. There is also a piece by the paleontologist Dale Russell on his collaboration with the artist Eleanor Kish in the creation of dinosaur murals for the Natural Museum of Natural Sciences in Ottawa, Canada. And there is another superb female artist represented: Margaret Colbert, creator of two dinosaur murals and wife of the noted expert on reptile evolution, Edwin Colbert (1965). So in this case, the paleontologist/artist coloration is familial as well as professional. The murals Margaret Colbert created depict the organisms found in the last Triassic Chinle Formation in New Mexico. The first mural was done in 1976 for the Petrified Forest National Park, and the second for the New Mexico Museum of Natural History in 1985. Even in the short period of nine years, a great deal was learned about the Chinle organisms so the second mural gives a much more complete picture of what life was like in this area in the Triassic.

Dinosaurs on the Move

Where to literally draw the line in recreating dinosaurs is a difficult problem, which becomes even more difficult when the images created are in three rather than two directions. In an essay called "Making a Dinosaur Work," William Jordan (1991) describes how life-sized dinosaur models that move are created by a company called Dinamation International. To make the beasts as accurate as possible involves collaboration among an artist, a scientist and an engineer. All three get together for what's called a "new creatures" meeting which begins with the scientific advisor to the project presenting what is known about the animal. Then the artist, often a sculptor, describes what the model might look like, and the engineer, who is responsible for creating the machinery that will make the "dinosaur" go, points out what is or is not feasible about that conception, keeping in mind the kinds of movements the scientist thinks were most likely for the beast. The Dinamation staff had originally thought that spectacular movements would be the most popular with spectators. They found, however, that subtle movements were more intriguing, and that the most important moving parts were the eyes. The fact that small movements are more effective was a relief to engineers, because these moves cause less fatigue in the urethane "skin" the animals wear.

Though I've heard about exhibits of Dinamation creatures, I was never tempted to see one, because I was still choosing to ignore dinosaurs. I am more familiar with the less flashy displays at natural history museums. Recently, I visited the National Museum of Natural History in Washington, DC, where there is a life-size *Stegosaurus* made of papier-mâché that has survived several reincarnations of the dinosaur exhibit (Yochelson 1985). It was originally made for the 1904 St. Louis Exposition, so it is a link to Hawkins' 19th-century dinosaur sculptures and shows the enduring fascination with life-size replicas. At the American Museum of Natural History (AMNH) in New York, the dinosaur exhibits consist mainly of skeletons, rather than skin-covered replicas. Some fossils are still partially embedded in rock, a good reminder of how most of these fossils looked when they were first unearthed after millions of years (Cooper 1996).

That's Entertainment?

The first complete dinosaur skeleton to be mounted was created for the Philadelphia Academy of Sciences. It was *Hadrosaurus,* which had been discovered by Joseph Leidy, one of the most noted biologists of the 19th century (Warren 1998). This skeleton was completed by Hawkins in 1868, almost 15 years after his dinosaur sculptures went on exhibit in England, so fleshcovered reconstructions were created before the less imaginative and more scientifically accurate skeletons. This fact and the Dinamation exhibits speak to the issue: Is the reconstruction of dinosaurs science or art, serious culture or entertainment? I think the answer to this question lies somewhere between the extremes. The "new creature" meetings indicate that neither science nor art can build a dinosaur single-handedly, that both factual information and an artistic sense are necessary, and that dinosaur exhibits do teach something about these animals while also entertaining spectators.

A trip to any natural history museum today indicates that the line between education and entertainment is blurred, if not invisible. In an odd book called *The Mammoth and the Mouse,* Florike Egmond and Peter Mason (1997) argue that such a line is impossible to draw and that this has been the case for a long time. They see connections among several events: Charles Willson Peale's exhuming a mastodon skeleton and exhibiting it in early 19th-century Philadelphia, the creation of Hawkins' dinosaurs, and the exhibition of the skeleton of another large beast: a blue whale that was beached on the Dutch coast in 1827. In all these cases, the exhibitors wanted to make money from science, so they advertised and did their best to make their exhibits attractive to the public. But at the same time, they were scrupulous about presenting scientific evidence as accurately as possible. These examples indicate that it isn't easy to answer questions such as how best to present science to the public and when does the replacement of substance by glitz become unacceptable.

Dinosaurs in New York

In AMNH, there is a spectacular reconstruction in the museum's great rotunda, the Theodore Roosevelt Memorial Hall. It depicts an encounter as it might have occurred 150 million years ago (Norell 1991). The skeleton of a female *Barosaurus* rears up to protect her offspring from an *Allosaurus* ready to attack. This is indeed a dramatic scene, poised between science and entertainment, and some critics think that the balance may have gone too far to the side of entertainment. *Barosaurus,* a herbivore, was one of the largest dinosaur species. Though *Allosaurus* was much smaller, it was a vicious predator, a carnivore that might indeed prey on young dinosaurs, though it wouldn't attack the massive adult *Barosaurus*. Would a reptile protect its young in this manner, or is this a case of playing to the crowd, of creating a scene that draws on human behavior to create human interest in a bunch of bones? Displaying a *Barosaurus* adult rearing up – to a height of about 50 feet – to protect her offspring is dramatic, but some researchers question whether it is an accurate portrayal of dinosaur behavior; it would have been difficult for its heart – even though it weighed about 800 pounds – to pump blood to such a height.

Other aspects of this exhibit also draw as much on art as on science. The bones are not bones at all but polyurethane foam replicas. They are used because the bones are too heavy to mount in the active poses used; a single *Barosaurus* vertebra can weigh up to 200 pounds. Also, the *Barosaurus* skeleton from which the casts were made was only 80% complete. In some cases, bones on one side of the skeleton could serve as models for those on the other side, but the shapes of some missing bones are based on the bones of the closely related *Diplodocus* about which more is known. When it came to the juvenile *Barosaurus*, much more was the result of guesswork because the only juvenile *Barosaurus* bones in the museum's collection were some neck vertebrae and a crushed skull.

The dinosaur halls of the AMNH were completely done over several years ago as part of a large vertebrate evolution exhibit that fills the fourth floor. The exhibit is both overwhelming and exciting because there's so much to see. The museum has a large paleontology research program at the present time and can also draw on the collections made by expeditions of the past. In *Dinosaurs of the Flaming Cliffs,* the AMNH paleontologist Michael Novacek (1996) tells of research he and his colleagues have done in the 1990s in the Gobi Desert of Mongolia. He also reviews the discoveries made by Roy Chapman Andrews, who led a famous AMNH expedition into the Gobi in the 1920s. Novacek blends travelogue with serious discussions of dinosaur evolution and puts his research and that of his colleagues into perspective. For example, he emphasizes the importance of the discovery not only of the large dinosaurs the public most enjoys seeing, but also small dinosaurs and mammals that help to fill in many blank spaces in our knowledge of the past.

More or Less Real

In *The Last Dinosaur Book,* a cultural history of dinosaur representations, W.J.T. Mitchell (1998b) argues that the more realistic a dinosaur reconstruction is, the less real it becomes and the more it is constructed by the human imagination. Adjacent to one of the AMNH's dinosaur halls are two exhibits from opposite ends of Mitchell's spectrum. In a glass case are fossils recently recovered from a site in Patagonia which is littered with dinosaur eggs; this is such a rich deposit that it's impossible to walk through it without crushing eggs. I had read about this discovery in *The New York Times* last fall – it was a front-page story, complete with a photograph of an extremely well-preserved piece of dinosaur skin found in one of the eggs (Wilford 1998). The *Times* article also described the fine state of preservation of embryos within some of the eggs. In the AMNH exhibit, there are three egg fossils that have been carefully opened to what lies inside. One egg contains the piece of skin pictured in the *Times;* the other two contain bones. To see anything more than pieces of rock, you have to look through a magnifying glass set into the case over each fossil. The piece of skin is then easily visible, but its tiny size is surprising, as are the sizes of the bones of the two embryos. It obviously would take someone with a good eye, the eye of a paleontologist, to spot such treasures.

These bits and pieces of dinosaur eggs are a long way on the real/realistic spectrum from the paintings on the wall just behind them. These are scenes from various stages in geological history, showing what the landscape would have looked like, with an emphasis on dinosaurs, of course. Done by Ron Barber, they show what the Earth might have looked like at several points in the age of dinosaurs. These small murals are the latest in a long line of AMNH representations of dinosaurs that include those of Charles Knight, who spent many years at the AMNH during the first half of the 20th century (Paul 1996). Several of his murals of the Ice Age have been restored and are now mounted in the museum's Wing of Mammals and Their Extinct Relatives. Although these murals represent times well after the extinction of dinosaurs, the murals do give a sense of Knight's artistry, including his exquisite use of color and sense of composition. Paul Semonin (1997) argues that Knight's 1942 *National Geographic* illustration of two *Tyrannosaurus rex* dinosaurs locked in combat helped to create the modern stereotype of these animals as vicious predators. And W.J.T. Mitchell (1998b) contends that Knight's dinosaurs unite "scientific novelty with kitsch, familiarity, feudalism, and modern technology" (p. 145). Mitchell sees the conflicts between dinosaurs that appear in these paintings as signifying the concept of survival of the fittest in an industrial society.

Scenes from Deep Time

Even before dinosaurs were named, artists had attempted to recreate the landscapes of past geologic eras. These attempts began after people became convinced that the organisms of the past were appreciably different from those of the present; in other words, that extinctions had occurred and old species had been replaced by new. This didn't necessarily mean that evolution had occurred – new species could have been created along the way – but it did mean that the landscapes of the past couldn't be presumed to be the same as those of today. In 1830, the geologist Henry De la Beche did a famous sketch of "life in ancient Dorset," in which he created a thickly populated scene with *Ichthyosaurs* eating other sea creatures, and even grasping a *Pterodactyl* as it flew above the water's surface. The vegetation consists mostly of palm trees, giving the scene the look of a tropical paradise gone mad.

In *Scenes from Deep Time,* the geologist Martin Rudwick (1992) traces the history of illustrations of past eras and sees De la Beche's image as the forerunner of a long tradition. Though Rudwick ends his review in the 1860s, it can be argued that this tradition continues to the present in paintings such as those of Barber. De la Beche's work remains influential in the sense that present-day paintings are still crowded with animals, to an extent that would probably not occur in nature, and the animals are clearly visible; there is no camouflage or attempt to hide. Also, it's often the case that the dinosaurs are presented in dramatic poses: grasping prey or at least chasing after it.

As Rudwick notes, one of the most dramatic scenes from deep time was done by the artist John Martin. His frontispiece for Gideon Mantell's *Wonders of Geology* (1838) is called "The Country of the Iguanodon" and shows three dragon-like dinosaurs attacking each other. The dark and menacing background adds to the sinister tone of the work. This romantic view of dinosaurs influenced many later representations of deep time, where landscapes are often dark, dramatic, and filled with strange beasts engaged in combat. This indicates the powerful influence an artist can have on the creation of scenes that usually appear only in science books and would be more likely to be termed scientific illustrations than works of art. But I should note that for many years after De la Beche's drawing, illustrations of deep time were often confined to frontispieces, because science writers were loathe to otherwise include such images in their work. Illustrations were seen more as art than science and therefore not appropriate for a "serious" work of science. This is a corollary to the real/realism issue, with science as real and art as creating a sort of false realism. Attitudes on the relationship between art and science have changed considerably since the 19th century. Now the publication in science journals of an important new fossil is often accompanied by an artist's reconstruction of the organism. This does breathe life into a sometimes rather nondescript-looking pile of bones – and wakes even people like me up to what's fascinating about dinosaurs.

References

Alvarez, W. (1997). *T. rex and the Crater of Doom*. Princeton, NJ: Princeton University Press.

Colbert, E. (1965). *The Age of Reptiles*. New York: Norton.

Cooper, H. (1996). Origins: The backbone of evolution. *Natural History, 105*(6), 30-43.

Czerkas, S. & Olson, E. (Eds.). (1987). *Dinosaurs Past and Present* (Vols. I & II). Los Angeles: Natural History Museum of Los Angeles County.

DeCourten, F. (1998). *Dinosaurs of Utah*. Salt Lake City, UT: University of Utah Press.

Egmond, F. & Mason, P. (1997). *The Mammoth and the Mouse: Microhistory and Morphology*. Baltimore, MD: Johns Hopkins University Press.

Jordan, W. (1991). *Divorce Among the Gulls: An Uncommon Look at Human Nature*. New York: North Point.

Mantell, G. (1838). *Wonders of Geology*.

Mitchell, W.J.T. (1998a). The hundred-story beast. *Terra Nova, 3*(2), 7-17.

Mitchell, W.J.T. (1998b). *The Last Dinosaur Book: The Life and Times of a Cultural Icon*. Chicago: University of Chicago Press.

Norell, M. (1991). *Barosaurus* on Central Park West. *Natural History, 100*(12), 36-41.

Novacek, M. (1996). *Dinosaurs of the Flaming Cliffs*. New York: Doubleday.

Paul, G. (1996, June). The art of Charles R. Knight. *Scientific American,* pp. 86-93.

Rudwick, M. (1992). *Scenes from Deep Time*. Chicago: University of Chicago Press.

Semonin, P. (1997). Empire and extinction: The dinosaur as a metaphor for dominance in prehistoric nature. *Leonardo, 30*(3), 171-182.

Warren, L. (1998). *Joseph Leidy: The Last Man Who Knew Everything*. New Haven, CT: Yale University Press.

Wilford, J.N. (1998, November 18). Dinosaur embryos show detailed fossilized skin. *The New York Times*, pp. A1, A28.

Yochelson, E. (1985). *The National Museum of Natural History: 75 Years in the Natural History Building*. Washington, DC: Smithsonian Institution Press.

The Biologist/Poet and the Poet/Biologist

I remember John Enders' obituary in *Nature* magazine because of the way it begins. F.S. Rosen (1985) writes that Enders died unexpectedly at the age of 87 just as he had finished reading a volume of T.S. Eliot's poems. Rosen seems to consider this a particularly fitting ending for someone who, though he had won the Nobel Prize for Physiology and Medicine in 1954 for discovering how to grow the polio virus in culture, had begun his academic career with graduate study in English literature. Enders was deflected from this path because his roommate was a student of the microbiologist Hans Zinsser, and it was Zinsser who reawakened Enders' early interest in biology. Enders ended up working in Zinsser's lab and getting a doctorate in microbiology for research on the tuberculosis bacterium.

Biologist/Poets

Zinsser probably got on with Enders because they shared a love of literature. Zinsser was himself a poet who for many years contributed poems to *Atlantic Monthly*. He is one of a number of biologist/poets. The noted essayist Lewis Thomas (1983) was an immunologist who also wrote poetry and in fact was publishing poems before he had any scientific publications to his name. The British neurophysiologist and Nobel Prize winner, Charles Sherrington (1940), published a book of poems, and the botanist Agnes Arber (1957) also tried her hand at the form, though she only published two poems. The most noted biologist/poet of modern times is probably Erasmus Darwin (1978) who wrote a number of treatises on science in verse, including *The Botanic Garden* which contains *The Love of Plants*. He was at the end of the British tradition of writing learned essays in verse form, a tradition that seems extremely quaint and "unscientific" today.

The most noted biologist/poet of the 20th century might better be called a poet/biologist, if his *New York Times* obituary can be used as a yardstick (Boxer 1998). Miroslav Holub was a Czech immunologist who produced a large body of poetry that is highly respected in the literary world, and his obituary focuses very much on his poetry and not on his immunology, though I don't think the two can be separated. Holub (1995) drew a great deal from his scientific knowledge in creating his poetry, but unlike Erasmus Darwin, his poetry is in no way didactic; rather, Holub employs science as a source of metaphors to enrich his poetry. In a poem on the heart he uses quite vivid descriptions of its anatomy to highlight its emotional nuances. His familiarity with the microscopic world comes through in a number of poems, as when he compares the death of white blood cells in an infected wound to soldiers on a battlefield: "...dreaming landscapes, lunar, derelict." Holub and his poetry were not popular with the Communist regime in Czechoslovakia, and many of his poems are about the treachery of those years and about struggles going on in the body politic as well as in the human body. But it would be unfair to characterize his work as purely political because it goes much deeper than that, dealing with all kinds of human struggles: medical as well as governmental, spiritual as well as political.

Holub is a master at creating memorable metaphors, which at least some students of poetry would see as at the heart of the process of poetry-making. But does this process have anything to do with making science? Is it just a coincidence that a few biologists also happen to be poets, and in most cases, not poets of the first rank? A number of those who have examined scientific inquiry as a creative process think otherwise. Jacob Bronowski (1966), who produced a book of criticism on poetry while he was finishing his doctoral dissertation in mathematical physics, sees metaphor-making as at the center not only of poetry but of science. His book *Science and Human Values* (1956) begins with a chapter on "The Creative Mind" in which he explains why the "act of fusion," of finding similarities between two seemingly dissimilar things or processes, is the essence of both poetry and science. Illumination comes from this comparison. Just as the great poets are those who can create the most telling metaphors, who can express the most basic human feelings in ways that ring absolutely true, so the great scientists are those who use metaphor to look more deeply into the phenomena of nature. Both the poet and the scientist deal with truth and use metaphor to get at truth, though they deal with different kinds of truth, different ways of knowing: truth to nature in science and truth to human experience in poetry.

Robert Root-Bernstein (1989) contends that while the types of truth dealt with in science and poetry may be different, the process of mental metaphor-making is essentially the same, and that the skill a scientist develops in creating poems can assist in making science as well. Poetry comes from a very deep place in the mind, from someplace almost beyond mind, where body and soul fuse. Getting to that place isn't easy, and it is even more difficult to remain there long enough to explore it. But this is the same deep place where the ideas of science arise, so familiarity with it as a poet can make it more accessible to the scientist as well. And there are other skills common to both endeavors. As Root-Bernstein notes, both the poet and scientist are intensely aware of words and their meanings. This seems obvious for the poet, perhaps less so for the scientist. But words are indeed important in science, though in a different way. While the poet is interested in the sounds and emotion and rhythm of words, scientists use words as "instruments of precision." Finding exactly the right word to describe a new idea or a new finding in science is essential to the precise communication that is at the heart of science.

Root-Bernstein argues that only through practice can someone develop the skills necessary to be a good scientist, and that this practice may not just be in science-related activities:

The difference between a technician and a discoverer is imagination. The only way to develop this trait is to practice using it. In short, to be creative, you must practice being creative. You must master ... 'tools of thought.'

And among these tools Root-Bernstein includes analogizing or making metaphors, which is obviously at the heart of poetry-making. But he also contends that developing such skills is not enough, that "transformational thinking" is also necessary, by which he means being able to use these tools in different contexts. Creating poetic metaphors will be of no value to a scientist's work unless the metaphor-making skills are transferred to thinking about scientific problems as well, but when such transfer does take place it can be a powerful aid to scientific creativity.

Since writing poetry is in part about pace, about timing, it creates a different pace from that of everyday existence and thus it can be said to create a different world. There is a sense of vertigo and thrill in stepping into this totally alien world, the world created by a poem. Doing science can also mean entering, and even creating, a very different world: the world of the cell, the world of the interior of the heart, the world of the surface of a protein. Great powers of imagination are required to explore such worlds, to "see" them as real and to discover ways to make the vision of them more distinct and detailed.

And there is something else about poetry: it is very structured. Even what is called "free" verse that doesn't seem to be written according to any rules often has an inner logic to it, and more disciplined verse forms have rhyming schemes and specified numbers of feet to the line. So writing poetry means more than just digging deep to find the essence of one's thoughts. It means digging deep and then working within very narrow confines, trying to fit ideas into a rigid structure. The mind has to work against a very unforgiving form and that forces the mind to work much harder, to dig even deeper, to find even more telling things to say. Writing poetry is difficult and this is where some of its attraction lies. It is hard to get a line or a stanza just right, but when it happens, the sense of rightness is wonderful. It happens rarely enough so as to always be exciting and to keep most poets' outputs very small. The complete works of each of my two favorite 20th-century poets, Elizabeth Bishop (1983) and Marianne Moore (1982), are just one volume, and even within what seems like a meager oeuvre, fewer poems still belong to the first-rank of verse. Digging deep can lead to the discovery of diamonds, but not very many of them.

Doing science also involves working within strict limits. Here the mind is not working against or within a rigid verse form, but within the bounds of the natural world. A scientist's ideas have to agree with reality; they have to match what is going on in the world. A hypothesis may be brilliant in its originality but if it fails to hold up in light of observation or experimentation then it must be tossed into the scrap heap of rejected ideas. This is what makes science difficult and often heartbreakingly frustrating; this having to measure up against reality is why any one scientist can accomplish so little in a lifetime. This is also what makes scientific discovery so exhilarating; it is wonderful when a large, perfect diamond suddenly appears after all that digging. Root-Bernstein would argue that this similarity between doing poetry and doing science is more than a metaphor that sheds light on each process. He would contend that the mental processes involved in digging, of working within tight confines, of working against narrow limits in creating poetry, are the same processes needed in doing science. The work performed in one context serves as exercise for the other.

Poet/Biologists

Besides the close relationship between creativity in science and poetry, there is another point of intersection between biology and poetry: the fact that many poets draw on the living world for inspiration, for metaphors, for images, and even for language. I would contend that there are not only biologist/poets, but also poet/biologists, those who are known primarily for their literary works, but who are also close observers of nature and readers of biological literature, just as biologists are. In the 20th century, there is Vladimir Nabokov who published significant work on butterflies, although he is much better known as a novelist and poet (Johnson & Coates 1999). But the poet I want to focus on is Samuel Taylor Coleridge. There is good evidence for the influence of science on his work, thanks to the digging of an early 20th-century literary scholar, John Livingston Lowes (1927), who set out to trace the sources of inspiration for Coleridge's two masterpieces, "The Rime of the Ancient Mariner" and "Kubla Khan." Lowes' principal source is a notebook in the British Museum that Coleridge kept between 1795 and 1798, the time during which the two poems were written. It contains notes on what he was reading and random ideas that he jotted down for future use. Lowes calls it a "catchall" organized "chaotically," but still, it is "one of the most illuminating human documents" in the museum. If it is that revealing, it is really Lowes' investigations that make it so; he wrings a tremendous amount of information from the notebook's 90 pages. It takes Lowes 400 pages of text and another 170 pages of footnotes to report on his findings. This may seem a bit much for poems that themselves only fill a few pages, but Lowes' book is fascinating because it is a detective story, as he digs into evidence for what Coleridge had read.

Lowes starts his analysis by taking just three stanzas and tracing the sources for the imagery found there. These sources include American naturalist William Bartram's book on his trip to Florida, Captain Cook's journals of his voyages around the world, as well as the writings of the chemist and religious dissident John Priestley, and the biologist/poet Erasmus Darwin. In the case of Priestley's work, Lowes is particularly dogged in his investigation. Lowes knew that Coleridge was an admirer of Priestley's, and while there is no direct reference in Coleridge's notebook to Priestley's *Opticks*, the book does contain a chapter on "Light from Putrescent Substances" with a description of a phosphorescent sea and of fish leaving luminous tracks, images that are also found in "Rime." But without any written evidence of a connection, how is Lowes to prove his case? First he reads all 812 pages of *Opticks* looking for clues. He doesn't find one until the last page where there is a reference to Benjamin Franklin's demonstration that two candles joined give a much stronger light than both of them do separately; this description appears almost verbatim in Coleridge's notebook.

With this citation, Lowes has shown that Coleridge had read at least the end of Priestley's book, but he still is not satisfied that Coleridge had read the whole thing. Lowes notes that:

> *it is notorious, as Petrarch wrote to Boccaccio in a famous letter, that the beginning and end of a book are often read, and the remainder skipped. May Coleridge, perhaps, not being spurred on by an obstinate quest like mine, have turned idly to see how the* Opticks *ended, and left its ample bulk unread? That, to be sure, would be unlike Coleridge; nor does the treatise exactly leave us on tenterhooks to know how it turns out.*

This passage gives some indication of why a reader would stick with the "ample bulk" of Lowes' book, and is followed by the clue he found that proved to his satisfaction that Coleridge had indeed thoroughly read *Opticks*, and in particular the chapter on "Light from Putrescent Substances." This chapter contains a footnote with a reference to page 213 of volume five of the *Philosophical Transactions of the Royal Society*. On this page is an excerpt from a letter written by a Father Bourzes, a Jesuit missionary, on "Luminous Appearances in the Wakes of Ships in the Sea." Lowes nails down his case for Coleridge having read this letter, and thus the reference to it in Priestley, by citing a passage from the notebook — "Sun paints rainbows on the vast waves during snow-storms in the Cape" — which closely matches a passage from Bourzes' letter.

This small segment from Lowes indicates not only Coleridge's persistence in hunting down references, but Lowes' as well. Lowes' book is filled with such evidence, carefully laid out to lead the reader from one clue to the next. By the end of the book he has made a solid case for his premise that a literary genius may draw from a vast variety of sources to create a masterpiece, and that in the process of creation, the source material is transmuted to make it the writer's own. Coleridge did not crib. Yes, he read widely and was not afraid to draw on his knowledge in creating poetic images, but each of these images has his unique stamp upon it, and many of them spring from a variety of sources welded together to create new images. What I find most interesting about this process is the breadth of Coleridge's reading. He didn't just read the sort of thing that was popular among educated British readers such as Erasmus Darwin's poetry or travelogues such as William Bartram's. No, he also tackled much more technical works such as Priestley's *Opticks* and the *Philosophical Transactions of the Royal Society.*

Much has been made of the Romantics' aversion to science, but that portrayal is hardly fair. Coleridge's familiarity with significant scientific works becomes obvious in reading Lowes, and John Wyatt (1995) has documented William Wordsworth's appreciation for the latest ideas in geology and how that appreciation found voice in Wordsworth's poetry. Yes, there are passages in both poets' work that indicate a wariness about science and how science changes our perceptions of nature, but these passages were not written out of ignorance of science but out of an appreciation for its negative as well as positive aspects. Science provided new ways of looking at the world — some of which were fascinating to both poets — and these new perspectives found their way into both men's poetry. Coleridge in particular deserves the designation of poet/biologist, not only because of his extensive use of scientific writings as sources for the images in his poems, but also because he went to the living world for the inspiration for a metaphor to characterize the creative process itself. He describes a work of art as a living thing, as being an organic whole made up of many parts that are well integrated and interdependent, with the whole being more than the sum of those parts, with a work of art growing and assimilating diverse elements as a living thing does. Philip Ritterbush (1968) contends that it was Coleridge's use of organic form to characterize the creative process that drew biologists' attention to the issue of form and spurred the development of the modern science of morphology. Ritterbush sees this as a case of art influencing science, and while biologists may be less convinced of this point, the fact remains that Coleridge did go to the living world when seeking a deeper understanding of his art.

Because humans are themselves living beings and because they are surrounded with other forms of life, it is not at all surprising that poets would go to the living world for inspiration. But the mental barriers between the disciplines are so profound that it still seems surprising to most people that two endeavors as seemingly different as poetry and science would have anything in common. Poets from the time of Lucretius have put the lie to this attitude. In the 20th century, many of the most noted poets were strongly influenced by science. While T.S. Eliot's ideas about science may seem rather negative, W.H. Auden was often rather positive in his portrayal of science. He was excited by the ideas of science and subscribed to *Scientific American* to keep up on the latest discoveries. Marianne Moore's (1982) poetry uses a great deal of animal imagery, and one of my favorite poems is Elizabeth Bishop's (1983) "The Fish." Even that 19th-century fish expert Louis Agassiz couldn't have asked for a better description of the external anatomy of fish than the one Bishop gives of a fish flopping around the deck of a boat. Fish seem to bring out the best in poets. The novelist John Hersey (1987) ends each chapter of his rather quirky book on bluefish with a fish poem. Trees also inspire poets, and so do spiders; there seem to be an inordinate number of poems about these beasts and their webs. In fact, a great variety of organisms serve as inspirations for poets, from Marianne Moore's rodent, the jerboa, to Mary Oliver's (1990) turtle.

But there is also a deeper level at which poets use biology in their work. They don't just describe living things, they also use biological concepts, discoveries about how the living world functions. Jane Kenyon (1993) has a poem called "Potato" that I love — perhaps because of my Irish background — but more, I think, because of its imagery. It is about peeling a potato and cutting off half of it and throwing it onto the compost heap because there is a rotten spot on that end. Every time she turns the compost, that piece of potato shows up, and it seems to get bigger, mocking her wastefulness in throwing away a lot more than she had to. In this seemingly simple poem, Kenyon has combined ideas about the cycles of nature with environmental responsibility, and all the time retained a sense of humor as well. Tony Hoagland (1998) has accomplished a similar feat in a poem called "Candlelight" in which he writes of the necessity of taking his wife out for a candlelit steak dinner in order to save his marriage. But he knows that the beef they'll eat came from a ranch in South America that's on land cleared by burning vegetation, and that the carbon dioxide thus produced, along with the methane produced by the cattle, is contributing to global warming. Even though he knows all these facts, and that they mean his grandchildren will, as a consequence, have to deal with a warmer world, he still feels compelled by his emotional life to go through with his "date." Here again there is a great deal of environmental science packed into a few lines of poetry.

But it is in the poetry of Pattiann Rogers (1994) that I have found the best examples of a particularly intimate knowledge of biology. She manages to tie concepts about everything from invertebrate zoology to paleontology into poems that are also very much about the human spirit. In "The Rites of Passage," she describes in detail the development of a frog embryo and links it to the origins of the universe. After reading this poem, it is impossible to think about embryology in quite the same way again, just as Jane Kenyon has forever changed peeling potatoes for me. I think this is the essence of the power of good poetry: to change the way we see the world and ourselves. I think this is also the essence of good biology. Knowing that genetics comes down to the twisting and replication of a symmetrical helical molecule makes inheritance into a sinuous dance, the perpetuation of traits from generation to generation cannot be seen in quite the same way again. Yes, doing biology and writing poetry are different endeavors, but it is important to keep in mind that this doesn't make them mutually exclusive — that they can and do nurture each other in a variety of ways — from serving as inspiration for each other to providing views of the living world that can enrich each other. By putting biology and poetry in separate pigeonholes we tend to ignore these interactions and thus make both poetry and biology seem less vibrant and fascinating than they are.

References

Arber, A. (1957). *The Manifold and the One*. London: Murray.

Bishop, E. (1983). *The Complete Poems, 1927-1979*. New York: Farrar, Straus and Giroux.

Boxer, S. (1998, July 22). Miroslav Holub is dead at 74: Czech poet and immunologist. *The New York Times*, p. A17.

Bronowski, J. (1956). *Science and Human Values*. New York: Harper & Row.

Bronowski, J. (1966). *The Poet's Defense: The Concept of Poetry from Sidney to Yeats*. Cleveland, OH: World.

Darwin, E. (1978). *The Botanic Garden*. New York: Garland.

Hersey, J. (1987). *Blues*. New York: Knopf.

Hoagland, T. (1998). *Donkey Gospel*. St. Paul, MN: Graywolf.

Holub, M. (1995). *Poems Before and After*. Newcastle upon Tyne, Great Britain: Bloodaxe Books.

Johnson, K. & Coates, S. (1999). *Nabokov's Blues: The Scientific Odyssey of a Literary Genius*. Cambridge, MA: Zoland.

Kenyon, J. (1993). *Constance*. St. Paul, MN: Graywolf.

Lowes, J.L. (1927). *The Road to Xanadu: A Study in the Ways of the Imagination*. Boston: Houghton Mifflin.

Moore, M. (1982). *The Complete Poems of Marianne Moore*. New York: Macmillan.

Oliver, M. (1990). *House of Light*. Boston: Beacon.

Ritterbush, P. (1968). *The Art of Organic Forms*. Washington, DC: Smithsonian Institution Press.

Rogers, P. (1994). *Firekeeper.* Minneapolis, MN: Milkweed Editions.

Root-Bernstein, R. (1989). *Discovering.* Cambridge, MA: Harvard University Press.

Rosen, F.S. (1985). John F. Enders (1897-1985). *Nature, 317,* 575.

Sherrington, C. (1940). *The Assaying of Brabantius, and Other Verses.* Oxford, Great Britain: Oxford University Press.

Thomas, L. (1983). *The Youngest Scientist.* New York: Viking.

Wyatt, J. (1995). *Wordsworth and the Geologists.* Cambridge, Great Britain: Cambridge University Press.

Learning in San Jose

The scholarship of teaching and learning is becoming a popular phrase in education today. It focuses on how we teach and on how students learn. But from my experiences last summer, it is also very much about teachers learning. I was fortunate enough to participate in a program called the Carnegie Academy for the Scholarship of Teaching and Learning (CASTL). There are two parts to CASTL, one for K-12 teachers and one for college teachers. The college program is jointly funded by The Carnegie Foundation for the Advancement of Teaching and The Pew Charitable Trusts. I was one of 40 college faculty chosen as Carnegie Scholars. We are the third group to be selected and we spent two weeks in San Jose, California discovering what the scholarship of teaching and learning is about and developing our own contributions to the field.

The "scholarship of teaching" is a concept proposed by the late Ernest Boyer, former president of the Carnegie Foundation, in his book *Scholarship Reconsidered* (1990). He argues that college faculty should not only be doing scholarship in their respective fields, but in the teaching of their fields as well. Such scholarship is one way to give more stature to teaching in higher education, where it is often denigrated relative to research. Boyer sees four components to this research. The first is *discovery,* that is, contributing new knowledge to a field. This is followed by *integration,* relating the new research findings with the present knowledge in the field. Then comes *application,* using knowledge, and finally, *teaching* or passing the knowledge on.

Since 1990, the term "scholarship of teaching" has evolved, in part due to the work of Lee Shulman, a professor of education at Stanford University and the current president of the Carnegie Foundation. Shulman (2000) differentiates between scholarly teaching and the scholarship of teaching. While the former means the kind of careful preparation that most would associate with teaching, the latter means doing research on teaching with the same rigor used in one's area of expertise. This is not easy for many faculty who have not investigated the education literature and feel uncomfortable with the idea of adding another aspect to their workload. The CASTL program is designed to help faculty understand the scholarship of teaching to the point where they can begin to contribute to such scholarship. To participate in the program, each of us had to propose a research project dealing with teaching in our disciplines. My project is on how students learn about images of cells and molecules, and I'll write more about it in the months ahead (when I have a better idea of exactly what I am doing).

Discovering CASTL

I got interested in CASTL when I attended a two-day symposium on this program presented at the 1999 annual meeting of the American Association for Higher Education (AAHE). There I heard two Carnegie Scholars give interesting presentations. Both were literature professors, John Webster of the University of Washington and Randy Bass of Georgetown University. They both spoke candidly not only of their projects for CASTL but of their problems in the classroom and how they attempted to deal with them. Webster found that when he returned to teaching after an eight-year stint in administration, the techniques he had formerly used just didn't seem to be working anymore. Bass's dilemma was that he found his student evaluations had plummeted when he used technological innovations in his teaching. This was particularly upsetting because it was his tenure year, and such innovation was a crucial part of his tenure case.

After talking about their problems, Webster and Bass discussed how they had gone about solving them, with both focusing – in different ways – on getting their students to be critical readers. They spoke of their fumblings – their right and wrong terms – toward more effective teaching and student learning. I found these presentations much more interesting and useful than the more common practice of giving a smooth presentation on some highly successful innovation. I find such "perfect" presentations unsettling, because the touted approaches are rarely that wonderful when I try to use them. It was comforting to hear two teachers, who were obviously very competent, admit that they didn't have all the answers.

When I told my boss, Julie Upton, who was the Director of SJU's Center for Teaching and Learning, about these presentations she suggested that if I liked CASTL so much, maybe I should apply, especially since biology was one of the disciplines from which CASTL was drawing applicants. Of course, when I was accepted into the program, she took full credit for my success, as did my husband Bob who argued that it was *his* proofreading that made all the difference. While I was willing to admit that Julie and Bob were helpful, it was really Bass and Webster who deserve credit because they are most responsible for my applying. I wanted to be part of a program that valued the wrong turns as well as the right turns in teaching, that saw the process of working toward better teaching to be as important as the product. Another reason I was so attracted to their work was that neither spoke of statistically significant differences between using methods A and B in the classroom, the standard approach to research in education. Webster used interviews with a number of students at the beginning and end of the semester to document the learning that occurred in his class, and Bass analyzed the e-mail messages students posted in online discussions as records of how their critical skills developed during the semester.

I was impressed by the fact that Bass and Webster both used student input in assessing their teaching effectiveness. This emphasizes the fact that CASTL is about the scholarship of teaching *and* learning. While Boyer coined the term "scholarship of teaching," it is Shulman and his associates at the Carnegie Foundation who have added "learning" to the phrase to highlight the increased emphasis in education on what is really being taught (Hutchings & Shulman 1999). The most exciting new teaching innovation is useless if it doesn't promote better student learning.

After the AAHE meeting, I read Bass's article on problems in the classroom which appeared in the first issue of the online journal, *Inventio* (1999). Here he discusses problems, and the fact that while having a research problem is considered a good thing, having a problem in the classroom is not so good and is something many teachers aren't willing to discuss. He explains why he thinks it's important to the scholarship of teaching and learning to share problems and attempts at solutions, that it is in the exploration of problems that some of the most interesting issues in teaching arise. He then describes one of the problems he had to confront: he realized that his most important objectives were not those that he necessarily focused upon in his teaching. This forced him to reorganize his course by beginning with the question of what it was he most wanted to achieve and then building the course around the objective, rather than taking the more traditional and content-focused approach. This made a lot of sense to me. It got at a nagging feeling I've had for some time that an overemphasis on content can make it difficult to achieve the deeper understanding and appreciation for science that I'm trying to achieve with my students.

Making Thinking Visible

Bass made a presentation at San Jose and began by admitting that he is on the CASTL "slow track," because he is a slow learner, and the more he learns about learning, the slower he gets. While one's participation in Carnegie's scholars program lasts a year and Bass was in the 1998-1999 group, his project still isn't finished — he's a man after my own heart. But despite his self-deprecation, Bass has indeed accomplished a great deal. He has reorganized his 19th-century American literature course so the emphasis is less on students' knowing a great many authors and works, and more on their becoming critical readers who are more aware of their own thinking processes. In developing his project, Bass has drawn on the work of Allan Collins, John Seely Brown and Ann Holum (1991) on cognitive apprenticeship, on "making thinking visible." They argue that in apprenticing to learn a craft, the skills needed are made obvious and are focused upon; while in the classroom, the thinking skills needed are often invisible, simply taken for granted. But better understanding, a deeper level of knowledge, can come from an emphasis on making thinking more "visible" by modeling the kind of thinking expected of students and by building a scaffolding, a support system for such thinking by asking questions and giving assignments that require deeper levels of thinking.

The concept of scaffolding took hold among the participants after Bass's talk. People liked the idea of a supporting structure to help develop critical thinking skills. The supports could be removed bit by bit as those skills developed, what Collins and his associates call "fading." Bass found the method effective in his course. He discussed what he called the "middle ground," the place where he could actually observe this deepening of understanding: in his students' online discussions. This was where the "texture of learning" was easiest to spot and to document because he had a written record. Bass argues that this is one effective use of technology in teaching, but that it is no substitute for classroom discussions and other teacher-student encounters. He sees such "hybridity" or mixing of approaches, where technology is one element in a course but not the only element, as the most likely and effective use of technology in education for some time to come.

Hybridity was also the hallmark of Dan Bernstein's research in teaching psychology. Bernstein is another 1998-1999 Carnegie scholar and his approach to the scholarship of teaching and learning is very different from Bass's. Bernstein uses a more quantitative research model. For example, he has done statistical analyses of students' test scores after a variety of different teaching methods he's tried in the past few years. He found that having students take electronic quizzes on reading material before class discussion of the material made for much more lively and interesting discussions, though their final grades didn't prove to be appreciably better. This result disturbed Bernstein, but in the tradition of the best scholarship, he has tried to find the reasons behind it. One plausible explanation is that the short-answer quiz questions were too different from the essay exam questions. The next time he teaches this course, he plans to add quiz questions that get at the more complex thinking that is required on the exams. It is this kind of trial and error that is at the heart of a great deal of research, including the scholarship of teaching and learning.

As was pointed out several times during the workshop, including in Bass's and Bernstein's presentations, the scholarship of teaching and learning can involve the kind of digging and slogging through problems that is encountered in all research fields. Bass contends that there are three layers to the scholarship of teaching and learning and that not everyone will necessarily dig down to the deepest level. The first layer involves having enough knowledge of this field of scholarship and its vocabulary to be able to explore evidence of learning in different ways. The second would involve using this evidence to design and redesign courses, and the final layer is reached when that evidence is made public and shared with colleagues through presentations, articles and course portfolios.

The Course Portfolio

The course portfolio was a topic that came up frequently in San Jose as a way to document and share the scholarship of teaching and learning. While teaching portfolios have been in use for some time (Selden 1993), the course portfolio is a newer idea. The teaching portfolio is broader and more philosophical in focus, containing a statement of the teacher's views of teaching and samples of course materials and student work that might be drawn from a number of courses taught over a long period of time. It is more an overview, while the course portfolio is a snapshot of a particular course, often for a single semester. The AAHE and the Carnegie Foundation sponsored a project on course portfolios, and the results of this project were collected into a book edited by Pat Hutchings (1998), a Senior Scholar at the Foundation and director of the higher-education component of CASTL. *The Course Portfolio* is a great resource because it provides firsthand accounts by a number of faculty who have developed portfolios in different disciplines and for different reasons. For some it was a way to provide evidence of teaching effectiveness for personnel actions; for others it was a means to document an innovative approach; and for still others it was a way to communicate ideas about teaching to colleagues. In most cases, the course portfolio, no matter what its aim, contains a brief introduction; some information on the course, including a syllabus, assignments and exams; as well as evidence of learning in the form of samples of student work and excerpts from evaluations, interviews or videotapes. One way this type of scholarship of teaching and learning is being made public is electronically. There are a number of web sites devoted to course portfolios; one of the best is for a math course taught by Theresa DuRapau at Xavier University in New Orleans (http://www.xula.edu/~tdurapau/portfolio.html).

The Choir

One of the problems I find with most workshops is that I suffer from information overload. There are so many interesting ideas presented and so much good talk at every meal that my head — with its very slow processor — easily overheats. That's when I take a walk or repair to my room for some quiet time to think. At San Jose, I decided to forgo several optional activities just because I wanted to have time to savor what I had learned and to figure out how to make use of this new knowledge. But there was one optional activity I'm glad I didn't pass up. It was viewing a video called "Teaching to the Choir: What's A Teacher For," produced by Indiana University's Faculty Colloquium on Excellence in Teaching (FACET). It is about 24 Indiana University faculty members who have won awards for their teaching and who go on a retreat during which Jim Mumford, the Director of the University's Afro-American Choral Ensemble and a faculty member himself, works to form the group into a choir. These were 24 people who were chosen for their teaching, not singing, abilities but by the end of the retreat each must not only sing in the choir, but do a solo as well.

This would seem to be enough of a story line to capture the viewer's attention, but interspersed between clips of Mumford at work with the group are interviews with some of the 24 participants about their reactions to the retreat and their views on teaching. Many speak of being fearful about singing a solo and relate this to students' vulnerability in the classroom. Professors of math and science talk about their approaches to getting at this problem with students who have repeatedly experienced failures in these fields. What works for these teachers is the use of group projects and designing tasks that give students a feeling of accomplishment. Another faculty member says that a mistake is not a blemish, but a window to learning – a very nice idea, but one that's difficult to keep in mind with scores of papers to correct. Still, it is this type of thought-provoking insight that makes the video so rewarding. Mumford and the faculty he is working with are the kind of educators willing to "take the extra two minutes," which is often all it takes to form a bond with a student that promotes learning, but they are not willing to reduce their standards. They are all working toward excellence, and while the faculty choir never sounds as good as the university's "real" gospel choir, they do sound a lot better than they did at their first rehearsal. Also, they feel differently about themselves and their roles as teachers in meeting the needs of their students.

I think this video qualifies as an example of the scholarship of teaching. It is definitely a public statement, and it provides insight into what makes some teachers exemplars. But for most of us, doing the scholarship of teaching follows along more traditional lines. As Shulman (2000) notes, scholarship involves reflection on a problem, documentation of an approach to solving the problem, assessing the results of that approach, and analyzing the assessment findings. This is not easy to do, especially when we have heavy teaching loads and other professional responsibilities. One of the great things about the Carnegie workshop was that it gave me time to at least begin the first step of the process: serious reflection. Like Randy Bass, I am guilty of not focusing my teaching on the objectives that I see as most important. For example, I want my students to understand why science is so difficult to do. But how much time do I really spend on this issue, and how effective are my approaches to getting this across? Answering these questions requires a great deal of thinking, of reflection.

And like Randy Bass, who was the moderator for the group of eight participants that I was assigned to work with on our projects, I am slow. Reflection, for me, requires time, and during my periods of reflection, I kept thinking of what I learned in one of the books we were sent before the workshop, *Understanding by Design* (Wiggins & McTighe 1998). It was a book that I found annoying when I was reading it because it seemed to be taking simple ideas and explaining them endlessly. But the fact that I kept thinking about so many of its ideas indicates that it struck a chord with me. Wiggins and McTighe contend that to design an effective curriculum, you have to start with the basic question you want students to be able to answer, what you want students to be able to do. Then the next step is to design assessment tools to measure the students' ability to answer that question and to perform as desired. This seems like putting the cart before the horse. How can you design assessments if you haven't designed the course materials and assignments yet? But they argue quite convincingly that it is better to know what you want students to be able to do, and then design the course materials that will make it possible for them to do it. Being slow, I haven't gotten very far with my design yet. I do have my basic question, and I am working on assessments. So I am on my way, with Wiggins and McTighe as my guides.

Reflection

Several years ago, when the concept of the "reflective practitioner" finally broke through the protective armor I wear against educational jargon, I was less than impressed with this idea. To me, it was just a fancy term for thinking, and it is that. A reflective practitioner is one who thinks about – reflects on – what has happened in the classroom and then uses those reflections to change her/his practice (Schön 1987). Isn't this just common sense, doesn't everyone do it? Well, yes and no. Everyone thinks, but for many people like myself, most of that thinking is wasted on trying to figure out what to cook for dinner and what chores have to be done over the weekend. In other words, most thinking is not very constructive. And I see this as a particularly American problem; we are doers rather than thinkers. We want to act rather than reflect. What the concept of the reflective practitioner highlights is that we can act more effectively if we think first – and second. In other words, think before we act and then think again – reflect on – how the action went, so that we can do it better next time.

The idea of reflection is also being used to help students to learn. It is more common now to ask students at the end of class to reflect on what they learned, on what they are confused about, on what most caught their attention. Many teachers now use Eric Mazur's (1997) technique for taking a brief break during class and asking students to work in pairs to answer a question about the material that's just been covered. This is a way not only to get at problems students are having, but also to get students to consider their own thought processes. This makes sense because, as came up a number of times in San Jose, students who are aware of their own learning processes, learn better.

As far as my own reflections on teaching are concerned, I was helped along by a number of readings that Pat Hutchings provided to all the participants. One was Howard Gardner's (1993) essay, "Teaching the Unschooled Mind," in which he discusses some of the difficulties in teaching for real understanding, including the whole issue of student misconceptions, which is familiar to many who teach in the sciences. One interesting misconception that came up at the workshop was more basic than a mistaken idea about a particular topic in science, and that is, a misconception about what a course should be. This issue was raised by Marilyn Repsher, who teaches math at Jacksonville University. She remarked that many students are resistant to her approach to math, because it is not what they expect. They expect to have to do problems, and when they are asked to write essays in math or to discuss the implications of a mathematical idea, they often think that they are not getting "real" math. I've encountered the same thing in teaching biology. Students expect to be fed a lot of facts, and when I want to delve into what it means to do biology, they are often resistant — they are disoriented because they are not getting what they came for. It was nice to know that this was a problem I shared with others.

In fact, a lot of the experience of being in San Jose was comforting in that sense. We were 40 people interested in furthering the art of teaching despite problems with administrators, colleagues, and even students. Some of us may be going slowly, but we are all on the road to exploring the scholarship of teaching and learning — and contributing to it.

Note: I would like to thank everyone at the Carnegie Foundation for the Advancement of Teaching for their support and patience, especially Lee Shulman, Pat Hutchings, Marcia Babbs, and the members of my project group.

References

Bass, R. (1999). The scholarship of teaching: What's the problem. *Inventio, 1*(1); http://www.doiiit.gmu.edu/Archives/feb98/rbass.htm.

Boyer, E. (1990). *Scholarship Reconsidered: Priorities of the Professoriate*. Princeton, NJ: Carnegie Foundation for the Advancement of Teaching.

Collins, A., Brown, J.S. & Holum, A. (1991). Cognitive apprenticeship: Making thinking visible. *American Educator, 15*(3), 6-11, 38-46.

Gardner, H. (1993). *Educating the Unschooled Mind*. Washington, DC: Capitol Hill Science and Public Policy Seminar Series.

Hutchings, P. (Ed.). (1998). *The Course Portfolio*. Washington, DC: American Association for Higher Education.

Hutchings, P. & Shulman, L.S. (1999, September/October). The scholarship of teaching: New elaborations, new developments. *Change,* pp. 11-15.

Mazur, E. (1997). *Peer Instruction: A User's Manual*. Englewood Cliffs, NJ: Prentice-Hall.

Schön, D. (1987). *Educating the Reflective Practitioner*. San Francisco: Jossey-Bass.

Selden, P. (1993). *Successful Use of Teaching Portfolios*. Boston, MA: Anker.

Shulman, L.S. (2000). From Minsk to Pinsk: Why a scholarship of teaching and learning? *Journal of Scholarship of Teaching and Learning, 1*(1), 48-52.

Wiggins, G. & McTighe, J. (1998). *Understanding by Design*. Alexandria, VA: Association for Supervision and Curriculum Development.

Living with Organisms

Last June, two articles about animals ran in *The New York Times* within a week of each other. On the face of it, this wouldn't seem odd, especially since there are often articles about animals in the "Science Times" section published every Tuesday. But both these articles appeared in arts sections of the paper. One dealt with the many TV shows featuring animals (Rutenberg 2000) and the other with animals in contemporary art (Boxer 2000). Both emphasized that animals have always appeared on TV ("Lassie" and "Mr. Ed" come to mind immediately to someone of my vintage), and there have been animals in art ever since there was art, namely the cave paintings of bison, horses and bears. But as the authors of these articles stress, there seems to be something new about the present interest in animals, an urgency and even an obsessiveness.

Perhaps the most famous examples of animals in the art of the 1990s are found in the work of the English artist, Damien Hirst, whose creations include a shark in formaldehyde (*The Physical Impossibility of Death in the*

Mind of Someone Living 1991) and a pig sliced longitudinally so that its internal organs are visible (*This Little Piggy Went to Market, This Little Piggy Stayed Home* 1996), to name just two. In a new show, Hirst is exhibiting, among other works, a 20-foot-tall anatomical model of the human body (Schjeldahl 2000). But Hirst is hardly alone in using animals in creating art. In a recent exhibit called "Unnatural Science" held at the Massachusetts Museum of Contemporary Art, Thomas Grünfeld exhibited a piece called *Misfit (St. Bernard)* in which the head of a sheep is attached to the body of a dog. More benignly, William Wegman has become famous for his photographs of Weimaraners in hundreds of different poses wearing everything from wigs to flippers.

These are only a few examples from a much larger body of work. As Sarah Boxer (2000) notes in her review of this art, animals are being used for very different reasons in such art. In some cases, it is to show the close connections between humans and other species. The fact that we respond to a dog in a wig is an indication of this. In others, the cruelty of humans to animals is obviously being highlighted, as is the fact that humans see animals merely as objects for human use. There is also the issue that so many of the animals with which humans choose to surround themselves are, thanks to centuries of selective breeding, essentially human constructs, just as are works of art.

Animals on TV

As to why animals are so common on TV, again there seem to be several factors coming into play. One is simply that shows featuring animals are popular. Animal Planet, which runs animal shows exclusively, is the fastest-growing channel on cable. A Discovery Channel show, "Walking with Dinosaurs," drew the largest audience ever to watch a cable program, other than sports or news. In his article on such programs, Jim Rutenberg (2000) notes that "on a typical day, the majority of cable subscribers are offered 32 hours of animals." He also observes that today's animal programs differ from those of the past. In the 1960s such shows typically were serious narrations with a heavy dose of information. These gave way to some gory and spectacular programs, and finally, to the shows of today that blend lively narration with more close-up photography, and include both educational and entertaining material.

Adding to the increased interest in animals on TV is the fact that with more and more cable channels, there's a need for more programming, and animal programs are relatively cheap to produce – the actors may be temperamental but they don't command large fees. Also, parents see animal shows as safe TV for children to watch. In addition, new lightweight video cameras make it easier to tape such shows and also produce better quality images with more close-ups, which are often the most fascinating elements of such programs. New technologies are also responsible for animals showing up with increased frequencies somewhere else: in TV commercials. This trend stems from an improved ability to manipulate images digitally, so dogs can appear to be grinning or moving their lips as if talking; bears can dance and drive SUV's; and frogs can sell beer. Again, as with TV shows, animals are put into advertisements because people have positive feelings about them. We see them as cute or funny or beautiful.

Life at Home

But it is not just on TV and in museums that animals seem to be proliferating; they are in our homes as well, where botanical specimens are also likely to be found. Of course, for many people a dog or a cat is an essential member of the household, and most people manage to keep at least one plant alive. But even for those who are pet-less and plant-less, it is unlikely that their homes are lacking in images of animals and plants. I have been doing some investigation of the biology of interior decorating lately, and this research has led me to conclude that it is difficult, if not impossible, to furnish a home without living things or their images. Even the most minimal of living rooms — one of those stark affairs with bare floors, bare windows, and two pieces of furniture — will usually have a vase of flowers on a table or a large tree in a pot; and often the windows look out, not on a city street, but on a beautiful landscape. But most of us do better that that, with flowered upholstery or rugs, oil paintings of thoroughbred horses or ceramic figurines of monkeys, wood carvings of lions or cat-shaped pot holders. Zoological — and botanical — prints are also very popular right now.

And then there are all the remains of organisms that are used in decorating: sea shells, deer heads or antlers, mounted butterflies and insects, dried flowers, bearskin rugs, elephant-foot umbrella stands, and tiger skin throws. I am not claiming that these items are politically correct, but they have been used in decorating in the past, and this use is one reason some of these organisms are now endangered species. Often such trophies were status symbols, signifying hunting prowess or indicating that their owners could afford these prizes or afford the trip to hunt for them.

Ecosystems at Home

Another way to look at organisms in home decorating is to take an ecological approach: there are home habitats where images of certain animals and plants are more likely to be found. Chickens and cows seem to belong in kitchens; fish and sea shells in bathrooms. You are unlikely to see a bear skin in a bedroom because it seems to belong in a den along with a deer's head; while fabric with cabbage roses is out of place in the den but makes a bedroom very cozy. If a room is designed for a man, then horses and deer and wild carnivores are appropriate; for a woman, floral prints and bird-filled patterns fit.

The ecological view can also be approached a different way. Many rooms or even whole houses attempt to recreate particular environments, sometimes, but not always, tied to the biology of their location. Homes in the Southwest are often decorated with cacti, images of desert landscapes, and representations of desert lizards or birds or snakes. An Adirondack cabin, on the other hand, is much more likely to have forest landscapes and images of fish or bears or deer. But the tie to the outdoors is far from absolute, with apartments in Chicago decorated with cacti, and forest paintings adorning homes on the Great Plains. At the moment, "country" décor is big everywhere, particularly in the houseclogged suburbs where chickens and cows would be frowned upon, but where representations of these and other barnyard species abound.

And there are other trends as well. In the last few years, *House & Garden* has run articles on shells, plants and insects in decorating. Biology seems to be "in" in the world of interior design. According to *House & Garden,* fish tanks are the rage among the rich and famous (Abramovitch 1997). One decorator now installs a tank in a wall where in the past he might have "hung a Roy Lichtenstein painting." The tank is cheaper, but not by much; some of the more elaborate ones can cost $35,000 or more. A 25-foot tank could be "swimming with moray eels, fluorescent blue tangs, and menacing-looking leopard sharks." And editor of *Tropical Fish Hobbyist* is quoted as saying that "people are getting tired of guppies and mollies. They want ecosystems in their homes: anemones, reef lobsters, corals and crabs. It's like diving in the Florida Keys." It seems that as we lose touch with ecosystems outdoors, we crave to bring them indoors – on the TV set, in art works, in fish tanks, and in designs on upholstery. Akira Lippit, a professor of cinema at San Francisco State University and author of *Electric Animal: Toward a Rhetoric of Wildlife* (2000), argues that as our culture has become more technological, there is a greater need for humans to reconnect with nature.

Biophilia

I would second this viewpoint: we surround ourselves with animals and images of animals because we need them in very fundamental ways that go well beyond entertainment. Here I am drawing on the work not only of Lippit but of two keen observers of nature – human and otherwise – who come from very different backgrounds and have different viewpoints, but still come to similar conclusions: humans need animals for their emotional as well as physical well-being and therefore humans seek to associate themselves with animals in a variety of ways. The biologist Edward O. Wilson uses the word "biophilia" to describe an innate human urge to associate with other species, with other living things. The idea of an attraction to organisms being innate is not surprising from Wilson, one of the founders of sociobiology who argued that many social behaviors are genetically controlled in a variety of species, including humans (Wilson 1975). In his book *Biophilia* (1984), Wilson elaborates on what biophilia is and why it was important for the survival of our species, because if this urge is innate, then it is likely to have some adaptive advantage. Wilson contends that attraction to other species would induce humans to observe animals closely, and the knowledge thus gained could be important in hunting and in protection against dangerous species.

Since *Biophilia* was published, others have become interested in investigating this innate urge, in proving its existence, and studying its manifestations. Stephen Kellert, a Yale ecologist, is foremost among these and, with Wilson, edited a volume of essays on biophilia (Kellert & Wilson 1993). Kellert has also published a book on biophilia called *Kinship to Mastery* (1997) in which he discusses nine aspects of biophilia, ranging from the very practical material needs organisms fill in our lives to their aesthetic appeal and the satisfaction of our desire for kinship and affection.

Roger Ulrich (1993), an advocate of biophilia, notes that the literature on biophilia has focused on people's responses to natural and urban landscapes, not to the indoors. But he has gleaned some interesting findings from studies that weren't done specifically to test the biophilia hypothesis. Hospital patients who had rooms with a view or with a landscape painting on the wall recovered faster, and dental patients who could watch fish swimming in an aquarium complained less of pain and distress than those who only had a painting or a blank wall to look at. Some contact with other living things or their images seems to have a calming effect – to fill a basic need – particularly in times of stress. These studies are hardly definitive, but they suggest the value of bringing nature indoors in some form.

Shaping the Mind

Paul Shepard (1996), whose field was essentially human ecology, does not stress the genetic origins of a human connection with animals as

Wilson does, but Shepard is nonetheless very forceful in his arguments for such a connection. He writes that:

> there is a profound, inescapable need for animals that is in all people everywhere, an urgent requirement for which no substitute exists. Animals have a critical role in the shaping of personal identity and social consciousness (p. 3).

Shepard's argument is evolutionary in a different sense from Wilson's. Shepard contends that since we evolved in a world filled with other organisms, the evolution of the human mind was very much shaped by interactions with other species in a variety of different ways and at a variety of different levels, from visual awareness to anticipating the behavior of other organisms. It stands to reason with these kinds of intimate relationships shaping human cognition, that if humans are then deprived of such exposure, particularly during the formative years, there will be a drastic and detrimental effect on the mind.

This is an interesting argument for saving the environment, and only one part of Shepard's extensive analyses of environmental issues, but I think it is something that as biologists we should be paying more attention to. Last month was my grandson's fifth birthday. After taking care of the scientific side of Scott's mind at the Nature Store, my husband and I went to FAO Schwarz to purchase "a few things" for the occasion. We *had* to get a Pokemon item, and decided that a small key chain was enough for that. We also bought a drawing set – for Scott's artistic side – and a sports game (so that he can grow up like his father – and grandfather). When we ran out of ideas we asked the salesperson who suggested Poo-Chi, a plastic dog that can bark, sit up, "eat" a plastic biscuit, etc., etc. Poo-Chi was a hit, and it turns out, not a one-day wonder. I had a letter from my daughter-in-law yesterday, and Poo-Chi is still going strong, with a few battery changes of course. He "sleeps" on a shelf over Scott's bed and is taken down every morning to be carried around.

While I'm glad Scott liked our gift, Paul Shepard's words make me a little worried about the long-term effects of growing up with a plastic dog rather than a real one. Scott happens to be lucky enough to live overlooking a beach in Bermuda, so he has more contact with "real" nature than many children do. But if feeling the heartbeat of a dog as he holds it is important to Scott's sense of life, holding Poo-Chi just isn't a substitute.

Years ago, I read something that made a lasting impression on me. It was in a book by William Gordon (1961) on synectics, a system that he developed and which was popular in the 1950s as a way to stimulate creativity.

Gordon found that college students who had been brought up on farms were able to create good metaphors more easily than students who were brought up in urban areas. He argued that many of the best metaphors draw on the natural world, and students with a farm background had much more intimate contact with and knowledge of that world, so they were able to draw on these experiences in creating metaphors. I see this as one small example of what Shepard is talking about — how contact with nature can shape the mind. But he is also getting at something much more profound than this:

> Animals and their representations constitute essential elements in human mental life: cognition and psychogenesis, individuation, personal and social identity, surrogate and symbolic figuration, and the conscious and unconscious iconic repertoire by which emotion and other internal states are integrated, coded and communicated. Animals connote fields of action and power — the objects of attention acquired during the evolution of human ecology as the neurophysiological structure of knowledge and speech (p. 72).

Plant-Human Encounters

It is interesting that Shepard writes of "animals and their representations," in other words, Poo-Chi and a panda poster aren't substitutes for the real thing but they are better than nothing; they are some reminder of what animals are like. And I should note here that it is not just animals that Shepard sees as important to human development. He also argues that plants function in a similar way to enrich the maturation of the human mind. He adds that, obviously, the plant-human encounter is different from the animal-human encounter, and this makes it all the more important since it makes for the development of different mental responses.

The anthropologist Jack Goody (1993) has written a fascinating book on the culture of flowers, and the use of flowers in decoration and symbolism since ancient times. He ties using flowers in decoration to the rise of agriculture. The growth of what he calls "luxury production" in the Bronze Age included the cultivation of plants solely for their blooms rather than their food or other utilitarian value, and once flowers became the focus of interest they were brought indoors and also became the focus of art. In Egypt, the lotus flower was a particularly important symbol and subject of art. Ernst Gombrich (1979) notes that even in pre-Dynastic times columns were often shaped to resemble lotus or papyrus lotus plants. Shepard would see all these examples as manifestations of a need of the human mind for the presence of plants.

In *Green Nature/Human Nature: The Meaning of Plants in Our Lives,*
Charles Lewis (1996) of the Morton Arboretum in Illinois writes about the
many ways in which plants influence our lives, from their therapeutic
value in hospitals and other healthcare facilities to their recreational value
in parks and backyards. Gardening is good for people for a number of reasons. It gets them outside, provides physical exercise, and perhaps most
importantly, it provides the kind of contact with plants that Shepard sees
as significant to mental well-being. Many people also bring the garden
inside in the form of houseplants, even going so far as to construct sun-
rooms where plants can thrive year-round.

Steven Kellert (1997) argues that it is significant that so many people
have plants not only in their homes, but in their offices where plants are
usually the only non-human species allowed. *The New York Times* ran an
article recently about an increasingly common trend of people bringing
pets to work, but I don't see that becoming a common practice. Plants are
a different story. A plant hardly turns a sterile office into a nature spot, but
it does at least serve as a reminder of the nature we crave. Nature posters
and landscape paintings are two other common office decorations, and
studies have shown that people with windowless offices are more likely to
hang up nature posters than those in offices with a view.

Problems

But while it may contribute to mental and physical health to surround
ourselves with reminders of living organisms, it might not be so good for
the organisms themselves. Some manifestations of biophilia in decorating
are damaging since the use of organisms or their remains can lead to
extinctions. Cactus hunters who dig up rare specimens for clients' homes
have endangered several species; leopard-skin rugs were once considered
desirable decorating accents — thus leading to the slaughter of these animals — as elephants and whales continue to be killed for their ivory tusks.

There seems to be an interior decorating fad right now for collections
of insects in glass display cases and frames. Doug Taylor of Praiseworthy
Antiques in Manhattan goes so far as to say that "bugs are so flamboyant,
they appeal to everyone" (Moonan 1998). He adds that a "good bug box"
costs from $50 to $500, and while it would seem to anyone who has dealt
with termites or carpenter ants that the supply of insects is inexhaustible,
insects too can become endangered, particularly butterflies.

If bugs can cost in the hundreds of dollars, the price of fossils can
range into the thousands of dollars and a lot more. While the insect craze

may threaten some present-day species, interest in fossils is a problem for paleontologists studying the life of the past. Those who hunt fossils commercially not only siphon off excellent specimens but often damage the integrity of the sites they disturb. Rex Dalton (2000) has recently reported on the farmers of Liaoning province in China who have made a lucrative business of digging out fossils from nearby rocky ridges. They often discover well-preserved bird fossils, most of which end up on the market rather than in the hands of paleontologists. But this is hardly a problem peculiar to China. Dinosaur hunters in this country are frequently at odds with paleontologists who see them as impeding serious scientific inquiry. In Morocco, trilobite fossils are the source of revenue, and some merchants are even faking fossils to cash in on the interest (Osborne 2000).

These problems provide one more indication of the powerful attraction other species exert on humans. As biologists, most of us are accustomed to thinking about animals and plants and studying about them, often in some depth. Most of us are very much attracted to animals and plants, and such an attraction may have been a big factor in our choosing to go into biology. But though we may love animals and plants, that's not usually what we stress in teaching about them; we discuss their behavioral characteristics or their development or their morphology or their relationships with other species. We do not get down to the deeper issues of why these facts and ideas are so fascinating, why spending time with living things is so rewarding. In other words, we ignore the biology of the very attraction that brought us into the field in the first place. What I am arguing here is that perhaps this issue deserves a little more of our attention because it is important for our students to understand this attraction. If they were more aware of it and its implications – more aware of the importance of organisms to their lives and well-being – they might have more respect for other species and be more committed to preserving the diversity of life on Earth.

References

Abramovitch, I. (1997, July). Object lesson: Aquariums. *House & Garden,* pp. 45-48.

Boxer, S. (2000, June 24). Animals have taken over art, and art wonders why. *The New York Times,* pp. B9, B11.

Dalton, R. (2000). Chasing the dragons. *Nature, 406,* 930-932.

Gombrich, E. (1979). *A Sense of Order: A Study in the Psychology of Decorative Art.* London: Phaidon.

Goody, J. (1993). *The Culture of Flowers.* Cambridge, Great Britain: Cambridge University Press.

Gordon, W. (1961). *Synectics*. New York: Harper.

Kellert, S. & Wilson, E. (Eds.). (1993). *The Biophilia Hypothesis*. Washington, DC: Island Press.

Kellert, S. (1997). *Kinship and Mastery: Biophilia in Human Evolution and Development*. Washington, DC: Island Press.

Lewis, C. (1996). *Green Nature/Human Nature: The Meaning of Plants in Our Lives*. Urbana, IL: University of Illinois Press.

Lippit, A. (2000). *Electric Animal: Toward a Rhetoric of Wildlife*. Minneapolis: University of Minnesota Press.

Moonan, W. (1998, August 21). Seeing beauty in the bug on the wall. *The New York Times*, p. E38.

Osborne, L. (2000, October 29). The fossil frenzy. *The New York Times Magazine*, pp. 70-74.

Rutenberg, J. (2000, June 29). Carnival of the animals. *The New York Times*, pp. E1, E8.

Schjeldahl, P. (2000, November 6). British flash. *The New Yorker*, pp. 104-105.

Shepard, P. (1996). *Traces of an Omnivore*. Washington, DC: Island Press.

Ulrich, R. (1993). Biophilia, biophobia, and natural landscapes. In S. Kellert & E.O Wilson (Eds.), *The Biophilia Hypothesis* (pp. 73-137). Washington, DC: Island Press.

Wilson, E.O. (1975). *Sociobiology*. Cambridge, MA: Harvard University Press.

Wilson, E.O. (1984). *Biophilia*. Cambridge, MA: Harvard University Press.

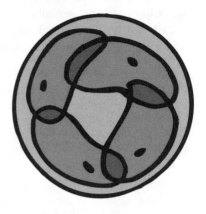

Being at Home in the Cell

Last semester, one of my students described me as "cell obsessed." I chose to take what might have been an indictment as a compliment. It seems to me that it is better to be obsessed with cells than with habit-forming drugs, gambling, or shopping on the Web. I will admit that this obsession is a long-lived one, having begun in freshman year of college when we were told to study a book of electron microscope images of cells. All that detail, all that complexity in something so small; it was then that I began to want to spend time with cells. I will also admit that my obsession may have intensified over the past year as I have become involved in a project with the Carnegie Academy for the Scholarship of Teaching and Learning (CASTL). As I mentioned in "Learning in San Jose," my project involves how students come to understand the images of cells and molecules they encounter in textbooks and in the classroom.

This is not a topic to which I have given a lot of attention in the past, despite my obsession with cells and an almost equal fascination with macromolecules. I just assumed that when students look at such images, they see what I see. But I have come to the conclusion that this is not true

— that this can't be true — because I have 35 years of cell watching backing up my processing of these images and they don't. This difference in background presents a problem, because while it is easy for me to see, for example, the relationship between an electron microscope image of a cell in which ribosomes look like little balls and diagrams that show the complex bipartite structure of a ribosome, it would be difficult for students to make a similar connection because they haven't lived through the history of increasingly sharp images of ribosomes as I have.

It is the question of how I can help students see a little of what I see when I look at cells, cell organelles, and macromolecules that is at the heart of my Carnegie project, though it is still evolving as I continue to explore this question. One of the things that has surprised me as I have worked on this problem is that answers seem to lie not only in the use of visual images, but with written texts and even with tactile exercises. Making models of cells and molecules gives students a much better sense of these structures as three-dimensional.

Seeing cells, really seeing cells, is a much more complex process than it may at first appear to be — to say nothing of seeing molecules, which I will leave for another day and another column. Here I want to explore some of the readings I've used or considered using to help my students appreciate cells as I do. I have come to realize that this appreciation — this obsession — is much more than visual or even tactile; it involves what I call being at home in the cell. I have come to appreciate more and more that the cell is a place I like to be, mentally if not physically. I can relate to Barbara McClintock's description of feeling as if she were down in the cell, being among the chromosomes; she was alone with her specimen and as one with it. It was from the unity that perception arose, that she came to understand what was going on in the cell (Keller 1983). This description rang true with me; it described an experience I've had, though obviously at a much less profound level. Looking through a microscope — or even looking at electron microscope images — carries me into a different world where I feel at home, and this is what I would like my students to feel.

What Is Home?

To accomplish this objective, which admittedly is rather ambitious, or even to strive toward it, required me to think about what it means to feel at home someplace. For me, being at home means to know a place well, to sense it not just with my eyes but by touch and even by sound. Home is a total sensory experience, and it is also an emotional experience because home means feeling safe and secure and at peace. In addition, it is an intellectual experience in that at home, I know where everything is. One of the most frustrating things about staying in someone's home is that I don't even know which cabinet to go to for a glass or where to find a tissue — things that I totally take for granted at home. This sense of place is also something a biologist develops in regard to the cell. If I am "in" the nucleus, then I know that I will find nucleosomes and histone molecules there; I wouldn't look for them in the cytoplasm.

But my lack of self-awareness was such that until I started to explore these issues for my project, I had never really considered precisely why I liked to study cells, to look at them, to spend time with them. As I explored these issues for myself so I could deal with them with my students, I found that I was originally attracted to the cell in part because of the sense of peace I felt when I was down in the cellular world. There I was detached from everyday experience, and all the cares attached to it. As I thought more deeply about these issues, and how I could get my students to feel at home in the cell, I realized that the best approach was from the angle of what they already know: a sense of being home.

Each semester, I ask students to write essays in which they must think through some question or issue related to what we are covering in class. For the first essay last semester, I asked them to describe the place where they felt most comfortable. I wanted them not only to describe the place, but to tell me how they felt when they were there, and why that place seemed so attractive to them. I got some of the best writing I've ever received on an assignment. I had hit upon a topic students could relate to, and in the process, I learned a lot about them. Almost half talked of their own rooms, but one student described spending time in an electronics store and another in her boyfriend's arms. Many wrote of feeling safe and secure in these places, and savoring time alone to do what was most important to them — listening to music, writing, or working on the computer. For several, spending time surfing the Web was similar to my spending time looking at cells.

Up to this point, I hadn't talked of my feeling of being at home in the cell. But when I did, after I handed these papers back, I felt that I could use what students had written as a basis for comparison: I feel about the cell the way you feel about your room. And I learned something about myself from this experience. I never had a room of my own when I was growing up — I slept in a room with my sister and worked at a desk in my mother's bedroom — and I found myself envying some of my students their privacy. Maybe the cell images I looked at in college were so appealing in part because the cellular world presented there provided me with a realm of peace and security that I didn't find at home.

But the important thing about this assignment was not only what I learned about my students and myself, but now I had a way to guide my students into being at home in the cell. I could refer to the place they had chosen as their safe haven and say that my sense of the cell was similar to their sense of their favorite place — it was someplace familiar and wonderful. They might still think I was cell-obsessed, but hopefully they now didn't think this was quite as strange as they had originally perceived it.

Readings on the Cell

To help them to think about the cell as more of a real place, as more than just a flat oval filled with squiggly lines as it is often portrayed in textbooks, I tried to come up with readings that might help them to feel more at home in the cell. What I was looking for were not necessarily information-filled sources. Many textbooks do a good job of telling students what they need to know about the constituents of cells and their functions. I was looking more for readings that would capture some of the awesomeness of cells and also give students a sense of what it is like to be inside a cell. As it turned out, I found more than enough sources to do the job.

The first reading to come to mind, because it is so visually interesting, was a chapter from David Goodsell's (1993) book, *The Machinery of Life*. There is a chapter on *E. coli* and one on baker's yeast, so I can have students explore either a prokaryote or a eukaryote. Goodsell is a molecular biologist but also an artist who creates very detailed and accurate images of cell interiors. They are absolutely stuffed with structures — this is what makes them so accurate. Cells do not have empty space, though this is the impression given by many drawings of cells. All the components in Goodsell's cells are drawn to scale, and their shapes are presented as accurately as possible.

While the drawings in *The Machinery of Life* are in black and white, Goodsell has more recently done colored cell images (2000). You can see some of the best, including a spectacular cross-section through a eukaryotic cell, on his web site (www.scripps.edu/pub/goodsell/). Goodsell's images are so detailed that they are sometimes difficult to read, but in the colored images everything is color-coded (proteins are blue, carbohydrates green, etc.), which helps. And even in their overabundance, these illustrations are useful because they are a reminder of just how complex the interior of a cell can be. They work well when paired with less detailed drawings of cells which can give students the basics of cell structure and make it easier to appreciate the more detailed images.

There is great writing about cells in both expected and unexpected places. One obvious choice is a selection from Evelyn Fox Keller's (1983) biography of Barbara McClintock, *A Feeling for the Organism*. There is a section in Chapter 7 where Keller describes McClintock's work on *Neurospora,* including McClintock's comments on being down with the chromosomes (pp. 113-119). The final chapter also gives a sense of how McClintock viewed her relationship to the material she studied under the microscope. As I mentioned earlier, no one describes being at home in the cell better than McClintock does.

Another of the readings that came instantly to mind was the title essay in Lewis Thomas's (1974) *The Lives of a Cell*. Here Thomas compares the Earth to a cell; both are exquisitely complex and both are made of many parts that interact intimately with each other. This is a great essay to use because it illustrates the usefulness of metaphors in understanding the living world. In this case Thomas is not creating a metaphor to help explain the cell, but rather using the cell to say something about the unity of the biosphere. In the same volume is another great essay, "Organelles as Organisms," about the theory that chloroplasts and mitochondria are the descendents of bacteria, which was relatively new at the time he was writing. A lot has been written since then on the subject, but there is something magical about Thomas's writing; he makes carrying bacterial descendants around in all our cells seem a truly wonder-filled phenomenon.

Also published in the 1970s, Larison Cudmore's (1977) *The Center of Life: A Natural History of the Cell* isn't nearly as well known as Thomas's but the first chapter is a very good introduction to the study of cells. Cudmore discusses a basic problem encountered when a cell biologist like herself attempts to share her wonder with others; it's simply that cells aren't visible to the naked eye. Admiring cells just isn't like admiring beautiful flowers or butterflies or birds; the cell isn't as familiar a part of daily life as these other organisms may be. Cudmore then tries to rectify this problem, using beautiful language to introduce the reader to her world of protists. My students, who — how shall I say it — are often less than thrilled with my choice of readings, loved this one. I think it may have been because Cudmore addressed the foreignness of the cellular world so forthrightly and thus articulated a problem that most students might not have been able to articulate, but nevertheless recognized as their own since she had found words for it.

Popular Writers

Another way to address the issue of the foreignness of the microscopic world is to examine the work of this universe's first explorers. There are many ways to go about this, including giving short excerpts from the writings of Robert Hooke or Antonie van Leeuwenhoek. Next semester I'm opting to use a chapter from a book that is itself a classic, Paul de Kruif's (1926) *Microbe Hunters*. Today, de Kruif's language appears dated; it is a bit on the flowery and dramatic side compared to the spare prose now favored in science writing for nonscientists. But it's not a bad thing for students to be exposed to a variety of writing styles. A number of the students in this class are communications majors, and we discuss how science is communicated to the public. *Microbe Hunters* was a bestseller when it appeared, so it's a good example of one approach to presenting scientific ideas to nonscientists.

I like to include a reading by Stephen Jay Gould almost every semester because, like Lewis Thomas, he is such a good writer. But Gould doesn't deal much with cells. In *Full House* (1996), he does emphasize the dominance of bacteria in the history of life on Earth; but apart from that, he sticks pretty much to the macroscopic level. However, in *The Panda's Thumb* (1980), there is an essay ("Bathybius and Eozoon") on cells, or alleged cells. It is about Thomas Huxley's *Bathybius*, a protocell that he thought he had discovered in ooze from the bottom of the ocean, and *Eozoon*, what was thought to be fossil remains of an early cell type. Both of these 19th-century "discoveries" turned out to be wrong, but that's one of the valuable things about this essay: it shows that even a first-rate biologist can be led astray. It also illustrates the powers of self-delusion and the tricks the imagination can play on observation. Huxley wanted to see *Bathybius* because he thought that evidence of the most primitive form of life would greatly bolster Darwin's theory of evolution.

Cellular Evolution

To go from the very dated to the latest research on cellular evolution, there is Mark Ridley's (2000) article on LUCA, the Last Universal Common Ancestor. He reviews the controversy over whether or not the first cell was similar to a eukaryote or a prokaryote. In a few pages, he packs in a lot of information in a very appealing way, making this a perfect reading for students. This piece was published in *Natural History*, which, in general, is a great source of readings, though most of the organisms discussed are of the macroscopic variety.

John Tyler Bonner (1994) also takes an evolutionary approach to cells in his essay "Becoming Larger by Becoming Multicellular." Bonner has spent his life studying slime molds that do precisely this. The essay is in a book called *Life Cycles: Reflections of an Evolutionary Biologist,* which is part memoir and part explication of the problems of development that Bonner has studied. I like this reading because it bridges the gap between unicellular and multicellular organisms, such as "Organelles as Organisms" bridges the gap between prokaryotes and eukaryotes.

Another essay that deals with the latter gap is by Harold Morowitz (1979): "Cell Types: The Great Divide" in *The Wine of Life and Other Essays on Societies, Energy and Living Things*. Though the title of this book is long, the essays are short and to the point. Morowitz's essays are fact-filled, and yet he conveys information painlessly for the reader. In the same book there is an essay called "The Smallest Free Living Cell," which is about the mycoplasma. Morowitz speculates, in the 1970s, on how big the genome for such an organism would be, how many genes are absolutely necessary for the life of a cell. This essay can be paired nicely with an article from a few years ago when the mycoplasma genome was deciphered (Bloom 1995).

While it may seem that I am using a lot of readings that may be dated, these readings are so good and so fit my purpose of giving students a sense of the cell that I am willing to deal with the fact that they don't contain the latest information. I can always fill that in, but I can't duplicate the wonderful descriptions these writers provide. Also, I sometimes find, as in the case of the mycoplasma article, that the fact a reading is somewhat dated can actually be an advantage. It provides a reminder to students of how rapidly science progresses.

But I do use some writers who are more current. I find Ursula Goodenough's (1998) essays in *The Sacred Depths of Nature* to be very succinct yet lyrical descriptions of the basics of biology. I've assigned her chapter on the origin of life but I could have chosen other chapters that deal with the basics of gene expression or evolution instead. As I mentioned in another column, this book is more than a review of biology for the nonscientist. Goodenough's central premise is that learning about the living world can be a spiritual experience. She ends each chapter with a reflection on this — how the biological topic covered in that chapter relates to awe, reverence, and other feelings she sees as spiritual, as sacred. I didn't assign this portion of the chapter I used because, quite frankly, I was more interested in the biology than in the religious aspects. But maybe I was wrong, maybe I should have assigned the whole chapter, and thus exposed students to another way of thinking about biology. I am always arguing that biology relates to other disciplines — that's why I use poetry and art in my classes — so why not include this brief foray into religion? The nice thing about teaching is that there is usually a next time, when the mistakes of the past can be corrected.

The Poetic View

In relation to poetry, the poem I chose for last semester was "The Conjugation of the Paramecium" by Muriel Rukeyser (1994). Though a book of poetry may be an unexpected place to find material on cells, poets such as Rukeyser can surprise us. I like her for a lot of reasons, including the fact that she wrote a biography of the 19th-century physicist Willard Gibbs, a seemingly odd thing for a poet to do. She is also someone who has written poems that are both significant yet accessible, and I think "The Conjugation of the Paramecium" fits into this category. It describes just what the title indicates, and the conjugation is used as a metaphor for human sexual intercourse in the most subtle and beautiful way. This was a poem my students were willing to read more than once, after they discovered that it was about more than a protist's reproductive habits. Rukeyser's poem is a good example of the power of metaphor to change one's views of both subjects in a metaphor. It's hard to think about intercourse or conjugation in quite the same way after reading it.

Also in the metaphorical vein is Kathleen Dean Moore's (1995) essay "Klickitat Creek" in her book, *Riverwalking*. This is a wonderful book and I wanted an excuse to assign a reading from it. On the face of it, this wouldn't seem to be a likely place to find a reading on cells because the essays are all about Moore's experiences — quite literally — riverwalking in the rivers, streams and creeks she and her family encounter on their hikes, most of which are in the Pacific Northwest. Moore is a philosopher and her husband is a biologist, so the essays blend — in a very memorable way — biological observations with reflections on how human beings relate to nature and the wisdom to be derived from that relationship. Fortunately for my cell obsession, Moore is such an astute thinker that she has even considered the various levels of biological organization and how they relate to each other. In "Klickitat Creek," she begins by using the naked eye to observe newts, and then takes her examination to higher and higher levels of magnification until she is discussing what is going on — at the molecular level — with sex hormones. Before ending, she climbs back up the size scale to come full circle and remind the reader of where she started, beautifully tying together a journey into the depths of nature and the depths of the human spirit.

I want to end with Moore because she has managed to do what I have tried to do in my approach to the cell: to link the cognitive with the affective, to present cells as places of wonder as well as of complexity. In an article I wrote a couple of years ago (1999), I developed what I called a "microscopic aesthetic" based on Aldo Leopold's (1949) essay on the conservation aesthetic. Leopold describes different levels of engagement with nature, and I argue that there are similar levels of engagement with the microscopic world, if we choose to devote time and attention to it. I have yet to assign this article to my students, but I might this semester because it deals with why the microscopic world can be an attractive place to spend time, in other words, why I call it home.

Note: I would like to thank Barbara Cambridge for her support on my CASTL project and Mary Jane Fortunato for introducing Muriel Rukeyser to me in a very meaningful way.

References

Bloom, B.R. (1995). Genome sequences: A microbial minimalist. *Nature, 378,* 236.

Bonner, J.T. (1993). *Life Cycles: Reflections of an Evolutionary Biologist.* Princeton, NJ: Princeton University Press.

Cudmore, L.L. (1977). *The Center of Life: A Natural History of the Cell.* New York: Quadrangle Books.

de Kruif, P. (1926). *Microbe Hunters.* New York: Harcourt, Brace.

Flannery, M. (1999). The conservation aesthetic and the microscopic aesthetic. *BioScience, 49*(10), 801-808.

Goodenough, U. (1998). *The Sacred Depths of Nature.* New York: Oxford University Press.

Goodsell, D.S. (1993). *The Machinery of Life.* New York: Springer-Verlag.

Goodsell, D.S. (2000). Biomolecules and nanotechnology. *American Scientist, 88,* 230-237.

Gould, S.J. (1980). *The Panda's Thumb: More Reflections in Natural History.* New York: Norton.

Gould, S.J. (1996). *Full House.* New York: Harmony.

Keller, E.F. (1983). *A Feeling for the Organism.* New York: W.H. Freeman.

Leopold, A. (1949). *A Sand County Almanac.* New York: Oxford University Press.

Moore, K.D. (1995). *Riverwalking: Reflections on Moving Water.* New York: Lyons & Burford.

Morowitz, H. (1979). *The Wine of Life and Other Essays on Societies, Energy and Living Things.* New York: Bantam.

Ridley, M. (2000). The search for LUCA. *Natural History, 109*(9), 82-85.

Rukeyser, M. (1994). The conjugation of the paramecium. In Jan Heller Levi (Ed.), *A Muriel Rukeyser Reader,* p. 2. New York: Norton.

Thomas, L. (1974). *The Lives of a Cell: Notes of a Biology Watcher.* New York: Viking Press.

About the Author

Maura C. Flannery's column "Biology Today" has appeared regularly in *The American Biology Teacher* since 1982. A favorite among *ABT* readers, it deals with critical science issues and how they affect our lives today. Flannery is Professor of Biology and Director of the Center for Teaching and Learning at St. John's University, Jamaica, New York.

She earned a B.S. in biology from Marymount Manhattan College; an M.S., also in biology, from Boston College; and a Ph.D. in science education from New York University.

She is married to St. John's history professor Robert M. Hendrick and spends her spare time writing, and quilting, her new passion.